∾ *Dr. Elizabeth*
The Story of the First Woman Doctor

∾ *Patricia Clapp*

DR. ELIZABETH
*The Story of the
First Woman Doctor*

Lothrop, Lee & Shepard Co. ∾ N E W Y O R K

〜 Books by Patricia Clapp

DR. ELIZABETH: *The Story of the First Woman Doctor*
JANE-EMILY
CONSTANCE: *A Story of Early Plymouth*

Printed in the United States of America.
1 2 3 4 5 78 77 76 75 74

Clapp, Patricia.
Dr. Elizabeth, the story of the first woman doctor.

SUMMARY: A biography of the first woman doctor written as if she herself were relating her struggles to become a physician and open the field of medicine to women.

Bibliography: p.
1. Blackwell, Elizabeth, 1821-1910—Juvenile literature. 2. Women physicians—Biography—Juvenile literature. [1. Blackwell, Elizabeth, 1821-1910. 2. Women physicians] I. Title.
R154.B623C55   610'.92'4 [B] [92]   73-17702
ISBN 0-688-40052-3
ISBN 0-688-50052-8 (lib. bdg.)

∾ This book is for J. P. and
all the Studio Players,
in spite of whose happy demands
it somehow got written.

❧ Contents

1	The Thought	9
2	The Decision	21
3	The Preparation	26
4	The Acceptance	35
5	The First Year	41
6	Blockley Almshouse	47
7	The Second Year	52
8	La Maternité	61
9	The Accident	73
10	England	78
11	New York	85
12	Emily	94
13	Kitty and Marie	101
14	The Hospital	109
15	The Hard Years	115
16	Paris	121
17	London and Home Again	128
18	The War Years	133
19	The College	146
20	1869. The Going	150
	Epilogue	155
	Bibliography	157

1 ∾ The Thought

∾ A doctor? I, Elizabeth Blackwell, a *woman* become a *doctor?* The idea is ridiculous! And yet—

Sometimes I wonder in what ways my life would be different now if I had been born at another time. Fifty years earlier, for example, around 1770 instead of 1821. Certainly I would never have entertained the notion of becoming a doctor during that century! Or fifty years in the future. Who can tell how the world may be then? Perhaps by 1870 it will not be unheard of for females to seek some other occupation than domestic service, schoolteaching, or marriage. Perhaps women doctors will not be unusual. But this is 1845, and I am twenty-four years old and obsessed with the thought of studying medicine. The reaction of almost everyone I know is a gasp of disbelief.

"But Elizabeth! You're a *woman!*"

And so I am. A small, shy, stubborn woman. A woman who, perhaps, has had too broad an education for the times in which she lives. Though the need for some social reforms is beginning to be recognized and aided by a very few, the overpowering majority of mankind has not changed its thinking since the century was new. I say "mankind," because "womankind" is not supposed to think at all. Certainly not of anything more important than domestic duties and childraising. Can I honestly hope to combat this solid wall of prejudice against the right of a woman to have a life—a *career*—of her own?

My family thinks so. But the Blackwells are not like most families. There are a lot of us, nine children counting myself, and when we lived in England (which will always be dearer to me than America) Papa insisted that his daughters be educated equally with his sons. This, of course, was unheard of! Instead of learning nothing more than household skills and a bit of music or sketching—subjects to equip a young lady to care for a home and husband—my sisters and I were taught languages and mathematics and geography and metaphysics and other stimulating studies which set us longing to follow roads that man-made tradition has closed to us. Papa always said he was fitting us for life, but not, it appears, for the life young ladies are expected to lead.

Papa was a sugar refiner, and during the years we lived in England, until I was eleven, our house was usually next door to or attached to his refinery. This meant that we often lived in dirty or shabby neighborhoods, which Anna, my oldest sister, seems to have minded more than the rest of us. She told me recently that she "utterly detested everything concerned with that constrained, held in, undeveloped girlhood!" Constrained we all were, and held in, but not, I think, undeveloped.

After Anna comes Marian, then me, then Samuel, Henry, Emily, Ellen, Howard, and George, who was born after we came to America. Papa was a Dissenter and therefore we, his children, were barred from the English schools. We had our lessons at home under tutors, and our heads were filled with far more learning than any schoolchild got. In addition, Papa's friends were those men whose intellectual horizons were stretched as wide as his own. We older children spent many evenings listening to men who dropped in to discuss various issues with our father. They talked of temperance, and better working conditions, of child labor and the abolition of slavery, of women's rights and improved institutional care in prisons and hospitals. All these subjects we absorbed and found natural. It was some years before we learned that most people did not share our thinking.

If Papa endeavored to stimulate and feed our minds, Mother's concern, then, as now, was with our immortal souls. She had a long list of things she felt would help to prepare us for a heavenly, rather than an earthly, happiness. Sober clothing, for example, lest we develop vanity; the simplest meals to save us from gluttony; hours of religious training, including stories of the devil waiting to snatch bad children, designed to prevent all misbehavior. Going to the theater would sully our souls, reading novels would fill us with romantic nonsense, and parties would encourage frivolity. It always surprises me to find that Mother approves of dancing, though I suspect she sees it as healthful exercise rather than entertainment.

Looking back now, I see that our early lives were governed by reform and religion. Papa placed more emphasis on improving the world we were in, Mother on preparing for the next. If Papa had lived I think he would have helped me wrestle with this decision now.

Seven years ago, soon after we had moved from New York to Cincinnati, Ohio, he died. I was sitting beside his bed, and I knew how ill he was, but when the hand I was holding lay totally inert in mine I could not comprehend his going. He was so dear to me! It seemed he had taken all hope and joy with him, and I felt alone in the world.

He left us with the house and its furnishings, and twenty dollars in cash. There was nothing else. That is when the schoolteaching began, from sheer necessity. Anna and Marian and Mother and I started a school in our house, and Samuel found a job in the courthouse in Cincinnati. Henry, who was thirteen, did most of the cooking. I don't know who was braver, Henry to do the cooking, or the rest of us to eat it. The little ones, Emily and Ellen and Howard and George, were still in their school years and could contribute nothing to the family finances, but somehow we managed. Since then Anna and Marian and I have continued to teach, though we gave up our own school when we received better offers from other places. Schoolteaching! No matter how much I dislike it, it is all I know. Would I dare risk leaving it to become a doctor?

This strange question of becoming a doctor started with a simple visit to a friend of Mother's, a Mrs. Mary Donaldson. I had just returned from a year of teaching school in Henderson, Kentucky, and joined my family in the smaller house we had taken in Walnut Hills, Ohio. In spite of all that Mother has taught us about being thankful for whatever gifts God in his bounty may bestow, I found it very hard to be thankful for being a schoolmistress. I was depressed and dissatisfied, frustrated and rebellious. It seemed as though there must be more for me in the world than the stupefying monotony of trying to beat the rudiments of knowledge into the heads of young girls who had no desire to receive it. The thought of endless years of this same boredom—years leading nowhere—was deadening. I tried to say as much to Mother.

"You shock me, Elizabeth!" was her reply. "God has given you good health and an excellent mind. Teaching is a proud profession and you should be grateful that you have the talent for it. Go and visit Mary Donaldson. It may make you appreciate your own life far more."

"Why? What has Mrs. Donaldson to do with me?"

"She is dying—slowly and wretchedly. Perhaps you can ease her by talking with her of the joys hereafter."

"Mother, I can't bear illness! I can't bear to be near sick people! You know that!"

"I know that it is time you stopped thinking exclusively of yourself, and more of the needs of others. Go and see Mary Donaldson, Elizabeth."

So I went. The poor woman looked dreadful, and the smell of sickness in the room turned my stomach. I sat beside her bed, stunned by her appearance, trying to think of cheery things to say, and tongue-tied by shyness and the distaste for her illness. At last she asked me how I had enjoyed the year of teaching in Henderson.

"I detested it," I said bluntly, my tongue loosened by my feelings. "It was bad enough working with those gawky girls all day, but Kentucky is slave territory, Mrs. Donaldson! Slaves! Do you know that I sat with my hostess in front of a fire one evening, and when it became overly warm I started to move my chair back, only to have her insist that a little slave girl stand between me and the fire to shield me! A little *girl!*"

She smiled weakly. "Poor Elizabeth. You are so much like your father. You would like to change the world, wouldn't you?"

"A great deal of it, yes. I should like to see slavery totally abolished! And women! They are not much better off than slaves, in many ways. I should like to see women free to pursue careers or professions of their own choosing. I should like to see women regarded as *equals* by men!"

"Is there no man who thinks of you—well, if not as an equal, perhaps as a wife, Elizabeth?"

"No. And it is probably my own doing." I paused, and laughed ruefully as I recalled an incident in Henderson. "There were many young people there," I told Mrs. Donaldson, "who seemed to like my company. We used to walk along the river on Sundays, and there was much idle silly flirting which everyone seemed to enjoy. One Sunday I became so impatient of it that I simply turned about and started off on a good brisk walk home."

"And what was the result of that impetuous move?"

"Oh, when the others returned they asked me in some consternation why I had vanished, and I told them I was bored by their sentimental doings. After that they did not ask me again."

She lay silent, gazing at me thoughtfully. Presently she said, "You are such a serious girl, Elizabeth. Are you going to *do* anything about changing the world?"

"What can one do?" I answered. "No matter how serious she may be, a woman can do nothing."

"Stop thinking of yourself as a *woman*, Elizabeth! Think of yourself as a *person!*"

"But they are not the same, Mrs. Donaldson. You know they are not."

"I know they will never be the same until someone with courage makes a move. Women have been sorry objects for years. They cannot vote, they cannot keep whatever money they might earn if their menfolk should demand it, they have no real jurisdiction over their children, they can own no property—oh, Elizabeth, I know all these things. But I can do nothing about them now. Nothing, that is, unless I can inspire someone younger than I. Someone like you, for instance. If you could choose your life—if you could order it any way you wished, what would you do?"

The thought was too big for me. "You mean—if I could do whatever I wanted?"

"Yes."

"Heavens! I don't know! Well—yes, I know the *sort* of life I'd like."

"Well?"

"Something that challenged me. Something I could waken in the morning and look forward to. Something that would make people—especially women—better off because I had done it. Something—but what difference does it make? I am a schoolteacher, Mrs. Donaldson. That is the fact."

She looked at me, her pain-colored eyes sunk deep in her head. "Why not study medicine?" she asked.

I stared at her. "I? Study medicine? You are jesting!"

"Not at all." She paused a moment, turning her head away from me, and when she spoke again her voice was wry with distaste. "You have always been blessed with good health, Elizabeth. You cannot imagine what it is like for a woman like me—ill and in need of medical care, but a *modest* woman—oh, Elizabeth! To have a doctor, a *man*, probing one's body, questioning one's most personal physical malfunctions! To have to expose oneself before a man! It would have been so much easier with a woman doctor. I could have kept some pride, some dignity, at least."

"But there are no woman doctors, Mrs. Donaldson!"

She turned back to look at me fully. "Is that to say there can never be?"

"*I* could never be," I said flatly. "I can't bear to *discuss* the human body! I can't bear the thought of sickness!"

She searched my face. "And you can't bear schoolteaching, and you can't bear slavery, and you can't bear the low position of women, and you can't bear the silly behavior of young people. What *can* you bear, Elizabeth?"

Uncomfortable, I rose and moved about the room. I could not think how to answer her. Certainly I was not offering the comforting thoughts of the heaven to come as Mother had bid me do. A row of medicine bottles stood on the table by her bed, and I touched them lightly. So much medicine, and none of it could help Mrs. Donaldson. How much doctors still had to learn.

"You should not be worrying about me," I said at last. "You should be finding joy in the prospect of a life everlasting."

"That speech came straight from your mother, Elizabeth," she said dryly. "And in a way she is right. The hereafter is all I have now, and I welcome the thought of it. There is so much pain—but I would be eased even more if I could believe my experience might make some other woman less miserable. You—

and other young people like you—are you going to do nothing with your lives? When it comes your turn to face the 'joys of the hereafter,' will you have left no record behind you? Sit down, child, I want to talk to you."

Reluctantly I went back to my chair beside her bed. She laid one hand, so thin it was almost transparent, on my knee.

"Elizabeth, listen to me. I lie here and think a great deal. There is little else to do. I think of my own life —such a weak and useless one—and of the lives of other women I have known. Often I have found myself thinking of you."

"Of me, Mrs. Donaldson? But you scarcely know me."

"Your mother has come often to visit me. She talks of you. I know more about you than you might suppose. For example, you have always liked to study, and you have had far more education than most young women your age. You are strong, and rarely ill. Yet you seem dissatisfied with your life. You feel it lacks a purpose. Am I correct?"

"I expect so," I admitted.

"For you there would be a twofold purpose in becoming a doctor. The satisfaction of being able to lighten the miseries of people like me, and the knowledge that you were opening a door that other women might enter."

"But why *me?*"

"Why not? Some woman is going to be the first female doctor, why should it not be you?"

I tried to find the words to tell her. "Mrs. Donaldson, soon after we came to New York I was in school there. There was a professor who hoped to interest the class in what he called 'the wonderful structure of the anatomy.' One day he brought into the room a bullock's eye! I can't tell you how hideous it was, resting on a disgusting cushion of bloody fat; I thought I would faint! How could someone so squeamish consider the profession of medicine?"

"You would learn to become objective, child. You would lose your squeamishness very quickly."

"But—oh, Mrs. Donaldson, forgive me for what I am going to say—but I have no *sympathy* with sickness! I don't mean that I am not sorry for you—"

"Never mind that. I understand. Just go on."

"Well, once as a child I had an intermittent fever, but I would tell no one that I was sick. It seemed contemptible and weak to *allow* myself to be ill! When the chills shook me I tried to walk them off, and when I could not, I shut myself in my room until they finally passed. Sometimes I used to go without food for two days at a time because I did not want to admit the demands of my body. There were times I slept on the bare floor—Anna and Marian thought I was daft—I wanted to harden myself! Don't you see? I have no patience with sickness!"

"What I see is that you have no patience with

weakness. That is a very different thing. Did you enjoy sleeping on the hard floor?"

"Of course not! I just had to prove that I could
do it!"

The deep lines of suffering in Mary Donaldson's
face shifted into a satisfied smile. "Exactly! And you
did prove that you could. As for having no sympathy
with sickness, I think that is a luxury no true physician can allow himself. An excess of sympathy can de-
stroy one's logic. Some people may see you only as a
small, quiet, shy woman, Elizabeth, but I think I
know you better. I think you have enormous strength.
Call it stubbornness, if you prefer, or sheer persistence.
Do something worthwhile with it, child! For my sake,
or for the sake of all women, become a physician, Elizabeth. You could do it—and I think you would make
an excellent one."

"But Mrs. Donaldson—"

"I am weary now, child. I must rest a while. Come
soon again."

I left her, my mind whirling and confused. Is it
true that I have done little but complain about my
life? Am I so lacking in courage I could never try to
break out of it? Do I deplore woman's lot and do
nothing to improve it? Am I resigned to going on day
after endless day with no more than the next class of
silly young girls to think of? If that is true, I am no
better than they! Was it for this Papa educated us?
What of the reforms he believed in so strongly? What

of Mother's insistence that we make ourselves worthy of the hereafter? To be honest I am far more concerned with the present than the hereafter! And the present poses a staggering question.

To become a doctor? Should I? *Can* I?

2 ∾ *The Decision*

∾ For weeks Mary Donaldson's suggestion has been revolving in my head. Her words certainly fell at a moment when I must have been particularly receptive!

Papa used to tell us to examine all the facts before reaching a decision. Very well, then. Fact One: I have had an excellent education, and I like to study. Fact Two: I may be especially small, but I am healthy and used to working hard. Fact Three: Schoolteaching bores me to distraction, but unless I break out of the accepted female mold there is nothing else for me but marriage. Fact Four: I am very confused about marriage! I frequently fancy myself "in love" with some young man, and delight in his company. Yet I have no social small talk, and when they go on about my "pale wheat" colored hair, or the intensity of my blue eyes, or my slim hands, I become impatient. Were I ever to marry, I should want a husband who could talk to me as a *person*. Someone who would recognize my mind, not simply my femininity. Also, as I have come to know more of what marriage entails, I am

often repelled by the thought of such physical inti-
macies. If I had some consuming interest which would
engross me, some real objective in life, perhaps I
could stop moping about in this discontented vac-
uum. Fact Five: Women are physically gentler and
more compassionate than men, certainly to be desired
in a doctor. Fact Six: Because of the complexity of
the female body, I think women are more aware of
and concerned with the physical functions. Fact
Seven: The easing of pain, the curing of illness, the
saving of a life—surely these would be the most re-
warding achievements a man or woman could desire.
And lastly, Fact Eight: If *I* could become a doctor,
the way would be open for other women to follow.

All right, what else? I am not timid, and I am stubborn. I have always wanted to prove I could do whatever I set out to do. I don't care a fig for social goings
on, nor personal fripperies of dress or adornment.
Surely these traits, which set me apart in current social circles, would be to my advantage if I were to
undertake this challenge. Now! Do I dare to try? I
don't even know where to start. Perhaps if I talked
to or wrote some of the physicians I know, they might
advise me. It could do no harm to take that small
step, I suppose.

I have written a number of letters to doctors known
by my family and me in various parts of the country,
and there have been two points on which all my cor-
respondents have agreed. First, that the entire pros-

pect of a woman becoming a doctor is unsuitable, un-
feminine, distasteful, and impossible. Second, that if
I were foolhardy enough to pursue this course I
would soon discover that no American school would
accept me as a student. Oh dear, that is *not* the way to
discourage Elizabeth Blackwell! The more I am told
"no," the more I think "yes."

But if I cannot study in the United States, then
where can I? I have asked this question of several
physicians, and the guarded answer has come back—
well, possibly Paris. I had an opportunity to talk
with a well-known Cincinnati physician, Dr. Muzzey,
and broached the possibility to him, knowing he had
spent some time working in French hospitals. I
thought his sparse hair would stand up straight on his
shocked head!

"Miss Blackwell! You surely are not serious!"

"But I am," I assured him. "Why should I not be?"

"The very thought of a woman going into the Parisian schools horrifies me! It's impossible!"

"But *why?*" I persisted.

"It would be offensive to both of us for me to go
into detail," he said firmly. "I will simply say that the
method of instruction is such that no American or
English lady could stay there for six weeks!"

And I could get no more information out of him.

I talk to everyone who will listen! One of my closest
friends is a gay and happy and clever woman named
Harriet Beecher, who has married a very dull and
stolid man named Stowe, and what they find in com-

mon I can't imagine, though there must be something for they have quite a number of children. When I mentioned my idea to Harriet she was stunned.

"Oh, Elizabeth! How could you ever do it? It's—it's so impracticable!"

"So I am constantly being told," I said. "But if I *could,* Harriet. What then?"

"If you could, I think it would be the very greatest boon to women!"

"I'm not sure what you mean."

"I mean women who are ill—or even just having babies, as I do—would feel so much more at ease with a female physician! And women who want to—to kick over the tight traces that tie them down would have an example to follow! But—how could you ever do it, Elizabeth?"

"I don't know," I confessed, "but I think I am going to try."

We have another family friend, an educated, intelligent man, James Perkins. When I mentioned the idea to him he neither gasped nor blushed, but simply asked me several succinct questions which I answered. When I had done, he said, with a very bright face, "I do wish you would take the matter up, if you have the courage—and you have courage, I know!"

At that moment I felt I could conquer the world! How far a little encouragement can go! He gave me a copy of Jackson's Memoirs which deals with medical training, especially in French schools. I am eager to read it!

A few day ago I did read it. What am I getting myself into? The immensity of the field before me is unbelievable! But someday some woman is going to do it. Why should I not be the one? I am gradually coming up to the resolution.

Enough of shilly-shallying! I have made the decision (Heaven help me!) and my family is in accord. I Will Become A Doctor!

My first necessity is money for my studies, though where and when those will take place I have no idea. For this reason I have accepted the position of music teacher in a school in Asheville, North Carolina. Teaching again! Ugh! But it is the only way I know to raise enough money to carry on this plan I have committed myself to follow. My main reason for accepting this particular offer was that the Reverend John Dickson, who is the principal of the school, was formerly a doctor and will start me on a medical education.

Mother would not accept the idea of her undersized chick making the journey to Asheville alone, so Samuel and Henry are to drive me there. I must admit I am relieved! I hear the roads through Kentucky are little traveled, and there are rivers to ford and mountains to cross—rather like the course I have set myself!—and it will take a good eleven days to make the trip. Henry is twenty now, and Samuel a year older, and they are such good company I look forward to this interlude with them.

Everyone in the family has been gathering books and other small comforts for me to take, and the carriage has been packed and repacked. Tomorrow, June 16, 1845, we will leave! I have never been so far from home before, and now, even before we start, I can feel the throat-tightening pangs of homesickness. But I feel something more, too. A deep, strong, inevitable force that leads me on, a purpose I must accomplish.

May God go with me.

3 ∿ The Preparation

∿ I have arrived. There were times, as Sam and Henry and I jolted our way over the Alleghenies, or forded a frighteningly rapid river, when I doubted we would ever see the end of the journey. Yet what fun it was! We sang, and talked, and picnicked by the roadside (where there were roads), and I feel I know my two oldest brothers better than ever before. As we came down from the last stretch of mountain onto the beautiful plateau where Asheville lies, I wished devoutly that the shared journey could go on, that Samuel and Henry would not have to leave me here —a forlorn little music teacher in a strange town, dedicated to a most dubious course.

I was very kindly welcomed by Reverend Dickson and his wife, and shown to my room, and for a while all was easy talk and hospitality. But then, that evening, no matter how I tried to hold it back, the moment came when I had to say good-bye to Sam and Henry, who were to start back at first light the next morning. Standing outside in the tranquil summer night I could find nothing to say that did not make the tears start in my voice, and at last I just kissed each of them and felt them hug me tightly for a minute, before I ran in the house and upstairs to my room.

I dropped to my knees before the open window. The surrounding mountains were dimly visible in the starlight, blurred by my tears, seeming to shut me away from all I knew or cared for, and suddenly I was terrified of what I was undertaking. I held tight to the windowsill, closing my eyes in an agony of despair, and whispering over and over, "Oh God, help me, support me! Lord Jesus, guide and enlighten me!" I must have crouched there for several minutes, praying, weeping, holding my loneliness and doubts deep within myself, yet reaching out for help, and then, suddenly, I felt as though my whole soul were flooded with brilliance! I felt a—*something*—around me, an influence, a presence, that was so gentle, so joyful, yet so powerful that all doubt disappeared! I can't explain this. There was nothing to be seen—I opened my eyes, but the room, the dark night, the dim mountains had not changed. Only I had changed, for I knew then, quite positively, that however insignificant my individual effort might be, it was in a right direction, and there was no more need to hesitate.

It was a most marvelous occurrence! I went to bed

and to sleep, and in the days that have passed since then, this new assurance has never left me.

Now that I dare to speak openly of my intention of becoming a doctor, it has resulted in benefits as well as teasing. Reverend Dickson has opened his medical library to me, and I read until my eyes are red with weariness, trying to remember the strange new terms and words—like a new language!—studying the charts and diagrams, and listening as this kind man patiently explains some of the myriad things I don't under-stand. I suppose it is an amusing contrast. During the day Miss Blackwell thumps away on the piano, guid-ing awkward young hands, asking for the same notes to be given over and over. During the evening Medi-cal Student Blackwell mumbles her way through the muscular system, repeating the terminology over and over. I do not know which is more likely, that my stu-dents will learn to play well, or that I shall learn to be a doctor!

Just yesterday I came close to discarding the whole idea. Another young woman teacher, who knows of my "unbelievable" ambition, brought me a large beetle, a cockchafer, thoroughly dead from having been smothered between her pocket handkerchiefs, and offered it to me as a first subject for dissection. Trying to look very businesslike, I placed the crea-ture in a small shell and held it with a hairpin, while I poised my mother-of-pearl-handled penknife for the incision. It was impossible! The idea of penetrating that small carcass was so repugnant to me that I could feel my hair growing damp with perspiration, and see my hand shake. My friend stood gleefully waiting, and I was on the verge of giving up when I suddenly knew quite simply that, like it or not, I had to do it. So I did. The knife point went in gently but firmly, and all it revealed was a little yellowish dust. After a moment, faint with relief, I felt larger than the mountains that surround me here! One small "beetle battle" had been won, and by me.

But what in heaven's name will I do when it is something more than a cockchafer into which I must thrust my knife?

Life here in Asheville is quite pleasant, and people are very friendly. Last week I attended a party with Reverend and Mrs. Dickson—rather reluctantly, I must admit, since parties have never been my particular forte—and to my amazement I found myself to be quite a social success! This was so unusual that it must have made me a little giddy, for I found myself chattering away vivaciously over the ice cream and whips and cakes and jellies; playing the piano with the top up and the bass pedal down; and even performing some tricks of logic, the sort of thing we do often at home, such as transporting the cannibals and missionaries across the stream.

There was one young gentleman from New York, attractive enough, but full of the silly, twaddling conversation that has always irritated me. He seemed quite beguiled by all my goings on, and insisted on escorting me home.

"You come from Cincinnati?" he asked, as we walked through the soft southern night. I admitted I did. "If I had only known!" he said. "I should have made the trip from New York to Cincinnati, just to accompany you here!"

He was tall and I am short and fortunately my bonnet brim hid the smile on my face. I could think of nothing duller than having him for a traveling companion!

"And you are teaching piano?" he went on.

"For a while," I said, and then could not resist the temptation to add, "I am going to become a doctor."

He stopped dead on the path. "A *doctor?*" he repeated, and his voice sounded a trifle weak. "What—er—what sort of doctor?"

"A physician," I announced calmly. "A surgeon, I expect."

He started walking again, but he said nothing for several minutes. At last he murmured, "Well! That's —er—that's very unusual, isn't it? I don't recall ever having known a—a lady doctor before."

"That's not surprising," I said with satisfaction. "There has never been one."

Poor young gentleman from New York! He walked me quickly home and left me. I neither blame him nor miss him!

The long walks that I love, I take by myself, because the young people hereabouts seem in mortal fear of treading farther than from gatepost to carriage. When I remarked that I considered eight to ten miles a stimulating afternoon's exercise, I thought they would swoon from shock. I admit that in this warm climate any exertion is not so attractive, but I simply slow my pace a bit, and enjoy the result. It seems equally impossible to find someone with whom to play such games as chess. Recreation that involves exercising the brain is as unpopular as the kind that demands exercise of the body. I set up the chessmen one afternoon and tried to beat myself, but it was not satisfactory.

I did manage to find a few people to share another enthusiasm with me, but it was short-lived. The wretched living conditions and the ignorance of slaves has always affected me deeply, and when I came here I resolved to teach as many as I could to read and write, but I found to my horror that the laws forbade it!

At last I succeeded in talking four ladies and one gentleman into having a Sunday school for the slaves, and slipping in as much extra teaching as possible. Unfortunately I did not realize their motives until our first meeting. As I looked around the room and saw those four ladies, all of whom were the wives of slaveowners, holding forth to the poor scrubbed, black innocents, and fancying that now they were fulfilling every duty and were superbly model mistresses, I felt such indignation it was almost impossible to sit still!

How can I teach a religion to slaves which their owners profess to follow, even while they violate its very first principles? I rage inwardly, but I have learned that any display of abolitionist feeling rouses all the southern prejudices. I am no orator, or I might try to convert them with a burst of passionate eloquence. Better, perhaps, to go on in my quiet way, doing what little I can, and knowing that it is not cowardice which keeps me still. There are so many injustices in the world, and at times I feel so small! I *am* small, but only outside. Inside I will *make* myself bigger!

Oh, the bother of having to earn money! It is the winter of 1846 and the Asheville school is about to break up. If I had any choice at all I should head for home and my family—it seems so long since I last saw them all!—but I have learned that I must have at least $3000 if I am to embark on a medical education, and therefore I must continue to work for a while longer. In one way at least I am in good fortune. Reverend Dickson has a brother, a distinguished physician in Charleston, Dr. Samuel Dickson, who, upon hearing of my hopes and my present financial situation, invited me to stay with him, to study under him, and to find a teaching position in Charleston, which he vows will not be difficult. This is far too happy an offer to refuse, and I will make the most of it.

On January 14 Mrs. John Dickson and I left by stage early in the morning, jolting off in bright moon-light over ground frozen hard and rough. After eighty miles of bone-wearying bouncing about in the stage that was partially eased by beautiful weather, invigo-rating air, and magnificent scenery, we reached Green-ville, where we spent the next full day. Following that, we traveled through undulating country where I saw palmetto, and the strange gray moss that hangs yards long from the trees, looking like giant cobwebs or the ghosts of weeping willows. After a night in the city of Columbia we made a rapid railway journey, which brought us to Charleston by two o'clock, where we were met by Dr. Sam Dickson's carriage.

Since my arrival, things have moved quickly. I have been given a rather tolerant encouragement in my perverse desire to become a doctor, and I spend two hours before breakfast each morning learning the necessary rudiments of Greek (since I already know Latin), and the evenings studying the medical books which Dr. Sam supplies. I have obtained a position as music teacher in a fashionable boarding school run by a relative of the Doctor's, a Mrs. DuPré, where at present I am giving lessons more than eight hours a day. The result of this activity is that I tumble into bed at night exhausted but exhilarated, and find my-self involuntarily playing scales up and down the covers with my fingers, while I mentally review Greek phrases or medical teachings. The days seem not long enough for all I must accomplish!

I continue to write letters to anyone I can think of who might be of help to me in furthering my doctor's education, but so far with little good. Even my family has, I think, begun to doubt the wisdom of my decision. I received a letter from my sister Marian recently which indicated as much, and wrote her back in this wise:

My mind is fully made up. I have not the slightest hesitation on the subject; the thorough study of medicine I am quite resolved to go through with. The horrors and disgusts I have no doubt of vanquishing. I have overcome stronger distastes than any that now remain, and feel fully equal to the contest. As to the opinion of people, I don't care one straw *personally;* though I take so much pains as a matter of policy to propitiate it, and shall always strive to do so; for I see how the highest good is eclipsed by the violent and disagreeable forms which contain it. . . . You also speak of my want of bodily sympathy being an objection. I suspect you were thinking of that unlucky dose of lobelia I once gave you when I grew angry because you groaned and groaned, and obstinately refused to drink the warm stuff that would relieve you. I think I have sufficient hardness to be entirely unaffected by great agony in such a way as to impair clearness of thought necessary for bringing relief, but I am sure the warmest sympathy would prompt me to relieve suffering to the extent of my power; though I do not think any case would keep me awake at night, or that the responsibility would seem too great when I had conscientiously done my best.

I have computed my earnings carefully, and I believe that by the summer of 1847 I shall be able to give up teaching and seek entrance into a medical school. The time seems as though it would never come, but in the meanwhile I study and study and study, and feel that I am learning much. I shall start in Philadelphia, since that is agreed to be the chief seat of medical learning in America, though prospects for my acceptance are dim. However, if I am to start—and I am!—I shall start with the best.

4 ∾ *The Acceptance*

∾The needed money has at last been gathered, and I am in Philadelphia a few months sooner than I had hoped, although for all the good that seems likely to do, I might have stayed in Charleston until I reached a hundred and ten! I have made applications to the four medical colleges in the city for admission as a regular student, I have been interviewed, laughed at, advised, discouraged, held up as a curiosity—everything! But I have not been accepted.

I am boarding with an admirable Quaker doctor

named William Elder, and his warm and friendly wife. Like many Quakers, Dr. Elder has attitudes and viewpoints that are quite liberal, and he takes a generous interest in my plans. He has even arranged for me to commence my anatomical studies in the private school of a Dr. Allen.

I think I shall never in my life (even though I reach a hundred and ten!) forget my feelings on the occasion of the first lesson actually to involve a portion of the human body! I sat waiting in a sweat of nerves, not knowing what was to be shown me, nor even whether I could bear to continue the lesson, but Dr. Allen—may he be forever blessed—chose as my introduction into practical anatomy a demonstration of the human wrist! I never before realized what beauty there could be in the exquisite arrangement of the tendons, in the clever joint, in the beautiful mesh of nerves and veins! There was such grace, such intricacy in the careful placing of each small part that it aroused a feeling almost of reverence. How divinely are we formed, and how marvelous the result! I think I shall never fear this branch of study again.

I had one interview with a Dr. Warrington, another kindly Quaker, who took me seriously enough to discuss my plan with an associate, a Dr. Ashmead.

"I mentioned to Dr. Ashmead the possibility of thy studying in Paris," he told me, "and I am forced to say he was against it."

"May I know why?" I asked.

"He regards it as such a horrible place, that if Paris

is thy only hope, he suggests thee give up all idea of a medical education."

"I have been told that before," I admitted, "but I cannot think a civilized city can be all that horrible. I should like to discuss it with Dr. Ashmead personally."

Dr. Warrington shuffled some papers around on his desk, stroked his side whiskers and avoided my eyes.

"I am afraid that would be impossible, Miss Blackwell. Dr. Ashmead feels that his communication would be so unfavorable that he would rather not meet thee in person."

I took a very deep breath and stood up. I am not very tall, but at least I am taller on my feet.

"Dr. Warrington," I said firmly, though I could feel my knees growing very unsteady under my petticoats, "I feel that the study of medicine is my duty, and if the path of duty leads me to Hell I will go there. I do not think that by being with devils I shall become a devil myself!"

Dr. Warrington stared at me a moment, and then rubbed a hand across his face. I was certain he was hiding a smile, and it made me fume. At last he spoke.

"There is one way, Miss Blackwell, but I have hesitated to suggest it."

"A way?" I sat down quickly. "And you haven't told me? A way to gain admission to a medical school?"

His face was serious now as he leaned across his desk toward me.

"Miss Blackwell, it is of no use trying. Thee cannot

gain admission to these schools here. Thee *must* go to Paris—and don masculine attire to gain the necessary knowledge."

I was bewildered. "But—but you just told me Paris was a horrible city!"

"It would not be kind to a strange woman. It is a city of fearful immorality where, if thee go as a woman, every feeling will be outraged and insult will attend thee at every step. But, if thee were to go as a man—"

I was filled with utter despair. To have a possibility, a way, a road, opened up to me thus, and then to realize that I could not accept it! Oh, it was cruel!

"I can't do that, Dr. Warrington," I said finally. "Don't you see? If I am to make any attempt at opening up to women the pursuit of medicine, then it is as a woman I must study it. Don't you understand? I would only be defeating one of my primary goals!" I half smiled, weakly, I'm afraid. "I have heard of hiding behind a woman's skirts," I added, "but I had never thought to hide behind a gentleman's trousers."

So that is that. And now where do I turn?

It is late summer and I have become so disheartened that I have left Dr. Elder for a brief visit with my family. Now, at home with them all, whatever doubts they may have had are hidden, and I am encouraged, made much of, spurred on, and given advice which, while I know it is probably worthless, is none the less welcome since it follows my own yearnings. Emily, the sister next after Henry, and now a handsome young woman of twenty-two, has been firm in her approval.

"If you will become a doctor, Elizabeth," she says staunchly, "I will, too."

"I should like nothing better," I reply. "Then we could go into practice together. But so far I have not noticed invitations of admission to medical schools coming at me from all directions."

"One will," she says warmly. "I *know* it! One will!"

"It had better be soon, then. Another few years and I shall have to be wheeled through in my Bath chair!"

Back in the City of Brotherly Love (but little Sisterly Love) there seems to be no help forthcoming, so I have enlarged my list of institutions where medicine is taught to include all the smaller schools of the northern states. After careful study of their prospectuses I have applied for admission to twelve of these "country schools," and now I sit back and wait impatiently. I am filled with anxiety because the time to begin the winter session is rapidly approaching. After all my brave talk, if I cannot start soon, *now,* I think my courage may fail me! Oh, Elizabeth! Why should you think *you* are the woman to lead women?

It has come!

Geneva, N.Y.
October 20, 1847.

TO ELIZABETH BLACKWELL, PHILADELPHIA:

I am instructed by the faculty of the medical department of Geneva University to acknowledge receipt of yours of 3rd inst. A quorum of the faculty assembled last evening for the first time during the session, and it was thought important to submit your proposal to the class of students, who have had a meeting this day, and acted entirely on their own behalf, without any interference on the part of the faculty. I send you the result of their deliberations, and need only add that there are no fears but that you can, by judicious management, not only "disarm criticism," but elevate yourself without detracting in the least from the dignity of the profession.

Wishing you success in your undertaking, which some may deem bold in the present state of society, I subscribe myself,

> Yours respectfully,
> CHARLES A. LEE
> Dean of the Faculty.

I must have read it through a dozen times! I wanted to laugh, I wanted to cry, I wanted to dance in circles or shout from the open windows! It was some time before I realized there was a second sheet of paper attached, and it kept shaking in my hands as I read it.

At a meeting of the entire medical class of Geneva Medical College, held this day, October 20, 1847, the following resolutions were unanimously adopted:—

1. Resolved—That one of the radical principles of a Republican Government is the universal education of both sexes; that to every branch of scientific education the door should be opened

equally to all; that the application of Elizabeth Blackwell to become a member of our class meets with our entire approbation; and in extending our unanimous invitation we pledge ourselves that no conduct of ours shall cause her to regret her attendance at this institution.

T. J. STRATTON, CHAIRMAN.

So it has happened at last!

On November 4 I left Philadelphia, hastened through New York, traveled all night, and reached the little town of Geneva in the late evening of November 6.

I am here, and now it is all to begin!

5 ❧ *The First Year*

❧ It is so cold! The wind whips off the lake until my teeth chatter, but on that first exciting, drizzling day I hardly felt it. After an impressive interview with the authorities of the college (during which I could almost see them shaking their heads in disbelief), I was duly inscribed as Student No. 130 in the medical department of Geneva University.

I found accommodations in a boardinghouse not more than three minutes' walk from the college along the high bank overlooking the lake, and set about making myself "at home." At dinner that night I could not help but perceive that a doctor's wife at the table avoided any communication with me, but it took several walks back and forth to the school before I noticed that ladies stopped to stare at me, or pulled their skirts close about them as they passed. Hurt and puzzled, I finally forced my landlady to give me the reason. It seems that I have so shocked the town of Geneva that I am fully believed to be either a bad woman or a mad one. I am not used to such unfriendliness, and it succeeds in making me feel smaller than ever. The one place where I feel at home is among my fellow students, though it took a great deal of courage to make my first entrance into the classroom.

I had carefully chosen a quiet gray dress, smoothed my hair back so it hardly showed under my bonnet, and clasped a handkerchief in my hands to keep them from feeling so clammy. Dr. Webster was the professor of this class in anatomy, and I was introduced to him before the opening of the class by Dr. Lee, the Dean of the Faculty. I gave Dr. Webster a note of introduction from my Quaker friend, Dr. Warrington, and then was told to wait in the anteroom while he read it to the class.

I sat and shook! If I had been able to walk directly into the class I think it would not have been as difficult as waiting. I could hear Dr. Webster reading the note aloud to the class, and I shut my eyes tightly and crossed my fingers as I listened.

As he finished there was a second's silence, and then a loud round of applause, and I realized my closed eyes were holding back tears. Dr. Webster came to the door and held it open, I entered quietly, the class rose noisily to its feet, I sat down, and the lecture started. I was in Medical School!

Just as I had begun to feel that in school, at least, I was wholly accepted, I was told I would not be allowed to attend a certain anatomical demonstration on the male reproductive organ. This annoyed me so that I wrote Dr. Webster, saying that I was a student with an earnest purpose, and as a student simply I should be regarded. I said that the study of anatomy was a most serious one, and the suggestion to absent myself from any lectures seemed to me a grave mistake. I also said I would yield to any wish of the class without hesitation, if it *was* their desire.

When I knew the letter had been delivered to him I went to the amphitheater where such demonstrations are held, but I prudently waited in the anteroom. Again, I could hear my note being read, but by now I had gained some faith in my fellow students, and I was not really surprised (but how very pleased I was!) to hear the hearty approval of my presence shouted through the door. Once more I entered quietly and took my place.

How little I knew what to expect! That dissection was just as much as I could bear! The embarrassment of all the students, increased tenfold by my presence, evidenced itself in varying ways. Some of them blushed, some were hysterical, not one could keep in a smile, and some who, I am sure, would not hurt my feelings for the world if it depended on them, held down their faces and shook. My delicacy was certainly shocked, and yet the exhibition was in some sense ludicrous. I had to pinch my hand till the blood came, and call on Christ to keep me from smiling, for that would have ruined everything; but I sat in grave indifference, though the effort made my heart palpitate most painfully. Dr. Webster, who had perhaps the most trying position, behaved admirably.

By the time I returned to my room I was thoroughly exhausted.

It would seem there are some members of the class who would like our association to be social as well as academic. I was making notes in the amphitheater yesterday when a little folded paper landed on my arm. It appeared to have writing on it, though I refused to look closely. I must admit I was curious! I should, indeed, like very much to have some *friends,* contemporaries with whom I could talk, and laugh, and—perhaps—even dance a little. I do love to dance! But I realize two important things. The first is that since I am representing "women," I must be the most perfect lady. If I am considered brazen for invading a man's world, then let me be modest in all else. The second thing is that I know myself! If it was a note, and if I read it, there would be need for some social gesture and before I knew it I might well think myself infatuated again. No! I brushed the paper from my sleeve without looking at it, though it took all my determination.

A moment later I thought I felt the lightest touch on my head, but I may have imagined it. The seats are rather close together, some student's sleeve may have inadvertently brushed my hair. I refused to acknowledge it.

The days go by quickly, and I am busy and stimulated, though lonely. This matter of being surrounded by young men from whom I feel I must keep myself aloof is constricting! On Christmas day I looked out my window at a beautiful world, clear and cold and sunny. The lake sparkled blue against the blue of the sky, and all the ground was snow-covered. My family had sent me the Christmas Annual which we have created for as long as I can remember—a collection of verses and stories and sketches by every member of the family—and I celebrated by spending a precious twenty-five cents for raisins and almonds. With these and the Annual I curled up in my quiet room and tried to remember that " 'Tis the season to be jolly." I may not have been exactly jolly, but I cannot complain. I am doing what I set out to do, and if the way is a solitary one, it is of my own choosing.

When I first considered becoming a physician I wondered whether my natural squeamishness might be a great obstacle, and—though I am surmounting it —it is. But in a quite unexpected way. I had thought that I might find myself repelled by suffering patients, by horrid wounds or a crippled body. But these I never see, since there is no connection between the college and any hospital. What does shock me are the instructors! Many of these doctors come directly to their classes from their hospitals, often after having performed operations. They take their places in the classrooms wearing jackets stiffened with blood and pus, and seem to glory in this evidence of their profession. I cannot think how they can bear it!

And their hands! They come from a dissection or an operation or the examination of a patient with no thought of washing. I have sometimes seen them wipe their hands on a handkerchief which might well be taken for a used bandage, and then restore the handkerchief to a pocket until needed again.

The newer doctors look with envy on the horrifying jackets of their seniors, and I know they are impatient for the time when their own clothes will look the same. I would not dare voice my repulsion, since it would only point up my female weakness, but I wonder if I shall ever reach that degree of medical sophistication which would permit me to stroll triumphantly through hospital corridors proclaiming in my dress the busy, bloody day I have spent. Not only do I find it an offense to the eye, but the stench is overwhelming! Is there no medical virtue in cleanliness? Apparently not.

For myself, I have taken to wearing a loose jacket, my "doctorial sack," over my dress, and this, I hasten to add, is always clean!

It is January now, and nearly time for this year's classes to end until next fall. It does not seem to me that medical courses are nearly long enough, but I am too new to venture such an opinion publicly. In any event, there is a general feeling of finality, and it has seemed to lower a few barriers. One of my classmates asked if he might write to me until such time as we start school again, and another asked if I would sit to him for a daguerreotype likeness. Both of these I refused, but gently.

I have attended my examinations, which were not very challenging, though a few of the students did quite poorly. My landlady, who has mellowed considerably in the time I have been here, and no longer regards me as a blot on the purity of her rooming house, invited me to an oyster supper—the first festivity I have enjoyed since arriving in Geneva.

As soon as I leave here I shall go back to Philadelphia to stay with Dr. and Mrs. Elder, and try to arrange for some form of summer study. Already I know I am going to miss school!

6 ❧ *Blockley Almshouse*

❧ I am back with the Elders in Philadelphia now, having decided to spend the summer, if possible, working at the great Blockley Almshouse, but I learned that the huge institution was so dominated by political party feeling that my only chance was to get both Whigs and Democrats on my side! This required a little careful management, but eventually I arranged an interview with the head of each party, unbeknownst, of course, to the other. These interviews were very favorable, and as a result, when my petition was heard at a board meeting, each side was prepared to fight on my behalf, but there was no one to fight! I am told this was the first time both parties had agreed on anything.

I have been given a large room on the third floor of the Almshouse, in the women's syphilitic department, which is the most unruly part of the hospital. I believe it was felt that my being there might act as a restraining check on the disorderly inmates, but what it does primarily is make them exceedingly suspicious of me. If I am not a nurse, and not a patient, then what am I? When I have tried to study at my table at night I have often heard soft footsteps outside my door, so I have now obligingly moved my table with the books and papers on it, and my chair, to a spot directly in line with the keyhole, where the "mysterious stranger" can be watched. This provides no answers as to what I am doing here, but seems to have lulled some suspicions.

When one considers that I am intent upon becoming a doctor and ministering to the sick, it is strange to think I have never been in a hospital before. It would seem to me that any physician in training should have the opportunity at some time to become familiar with such institutions, but instead medical school seems to be only lectures, lessons, and some occasional observation. All practical work is done during the non-school periods.

In any event, I am bewildered by all there is to see and learn here at Blockley. On the whole it is a depressing place, in some ways even frightening. Chill walls and floors that seem to hold the dampness, even with the large fireplaces that overheat those patients nearest them, and leave the farther ones shivering. There is the casual disregard for cleanliness and sanitation, evidenced by bloodspattered aprons on the nurses, surgeons wearing jackets as filthy as those I saw in Geneva, buckets of slop and vomit left unemptied for far too long.

There are the great jars filled with shining black leeches which seem to be preferred now for bleeding patients. I *know* I would much rather have the neat small knife incision in a vein than be covered with the limp slimy creatures, clustered in a gently moving mass, greedily gorging themselves on blood. I have been taught that bloodletting is of recognized good, but the leeches are so horrible!

While some few of the surgeons use the new ether for their operations, declaring it a boon to mankind, there are others who regard it as a newfangled experiment, and therefore suspicious. These doctors prefer to perform operations by dosing the patient with opium and then working at top speed. On some occasions the deadening effects of the opium wear off before the operation is quite complete, and the shrieks and groans from the operating theater are blood-chilling.

I find violently disturbing, too, many of the medical cases. There are a great many syphilitic patients here, and some of them are almost obscene to look upon! It is my first meeting with such diseases (it is my first meeting with so *many* things!) and how truly awful they are! Running sores that will not heal, ulcers on the scalp which cause bald spots to appear—and treatment with no known cure.

One young woman, badly infected, tried to escape from Blockley by tying sheets together and fastening them to the window, but they gave way and she fell from the third floor. She was brought back into the hospital suffering from concussion of the brain, broken bones, and other injuries. If only more women were aware of the hideous damage such diseases can do, they could be instrumental in controlling them, but it "is not proper" for them to know! I am more aware every day of how much good women could do in the world, if they were only given education and opportunity.

Dr. Benedict, the medical head of the hospital, has been most kind, giving me every facility in his power and free entry into all the women's wards. The nurses also are very friendly toward me, but not so the young resident physicians. When I walk into the wards, they walk out. They have ceased writing the diagnosis and treatment of each patient on the card which hangs on the head of the bed, so that I am thrown entirely on my own resources for clinical study. How much I am resented by some people! I should think it would take far more energy than is worth spending on one small female.

There has been an epidemic of famine fever, a form of typhus. This started in Ireland and was brought here by multitudes of emigrants who were attacked by it during the ocean crossing. So many of them have been brought to Blockley that we have been hard put to find space to lay them. Dozens have been placed on mattresses on the floor, and I tread carefully lest I step on an outflung hand or an uncovered foot.

The death rate from the disease is high, and the mortuary became so filled with bodies waiting for relatives to claim them for burial that many had to be heaped in an open courtyard. A few are removed to the dissecting room, but others remain until some burial can be arranged. The odor that comes in through the open windows is almost insupportable, and the flies that gather fill the air with a humming sound until it almost seems that the fever from which these poor souls died is a tangible thing that works its way back into the hospital again. However, no one else seems to be disturbed by this, and I can only assume it is my own fastidiousness that makes it offensive.

The hospital days are long and hard and tiring, but I have learned much during the summer here, and the practical experience has been invaluable. It will soon be time to return to Geneva, to take my place again in that exclusively male atmosphere which many young women might envy me. I feel always a little apart, always a little lonely, but now, at least, I am accepted, since we are all equal in what is most important to us, the study of medicine. It is good to be a woman who can share such ambition with men.

7 ∾ The Second Year

∾ Arriving back at the boardinghouse and walking into my classroom has been almost like coming home! Everything has seemed so pleasantly familiar and secure. The students are truly my friends, and I can now be more myself with them than with anyone else except my family.

Last Sunday a member of my real family made an unexpected and oh, so welcome appearance. Howard, the next to the youngest, came a-calling, and what a wonderful day we had! He is close to eighteen now, high-spirited and full of fun, but also a good listener, and interested in other people. I stayed away from afternoon classes to be with him, something I never believed I would do, and laughed more than I have in months. He asked a lot of questions, including what I had learned in the Blockley Almshouse. I hesitated.

"Well," I began slowly, "how little I know, I suppose."

"After only one year of medical training, I don't think that is so surprising," Howy said.

"Perhaps what I mean is, how little a doctor knows. A *trained* doctor. Even—" I smiled, "even a *male* doctor!"

"Male doctors know *everything*," Howard teased. "I will not allow you to malign my sex."

"They don't know of any sure way to bring children safely through the most common childhood diseases," I said. "Do you realize that as many children die as recover? Of things like measles, and whooping cough, and the throat distemper that flushes them scarlet and raises a scorching fever? There are no true cures for these things, only prescribed treatment which may or may not be effective."

"But I hear an inoculation for smallpox has been found, and didn't that kill off even more? Or leave them scarred for life?"

"Yes, perhaps it did. But only one answer? There must be ways to cure these other things too, Howy! Do you know the number of cases of ague that are treated but never cured? And intermittent fevers, and remittent fevers, and dysentery, and diarrhea—these *kill* people! And doctors don't know how to combat them!"

"But Dr. Elizabeth will surely find all the answers —just give her a little time." Howy grinned at me.

"There isn't that much time," I said gloomily, and then laughed at my own tone of voice. "In any event,"

DR. ELIZABETH · 54

I finished, "this *lady* doctor will know as much as the Magnificent Males, though she may not know more. That in itself is a wonderful thing for a lowly woman."

We had a satisfying day together! Outside of my classes my life has been so very solitary—I am not complaining, just stating!—but a whole day in Howard's lively company made an enormous difference!

All of yesterday, a bleak November day, I spent alone in my room, yet I was far from lonely. I thought a great deal about this course I am pursuing, and of my part in it. I know now I shall be a competent physician, but probably never a really talented one. That remarkable *insight* which sets certain doctors apart and ahead of others seems to be lacking in me. But I can learn and I can teach, and I think my greatest contribution (once I can claim that magical title, "Dr. Blackwell"!) may be in educating women into some of the things I am learning.

For example, the syphilitic patients I saw at Blockley. Because of the strict taboos that are placed on general sexual knowledge, I would wager that virtually no "nice young lady" has any understanding of syphilis. How can they know that one brief encounter with an unclean woman can so infect a man that he can spread the rot to any number of other women? I didn't know it myself until I started medical training. But women *must* be told these things in order to protect themselves! If I can make them aware of the dreadful effects of the disease, of the hideous chancres that form on the body, of the definite possibility of blindness or brain damage, of the fact that there is no known cure! They may turn away from me in disgust and disbelief, but somehow they must be taught!

I practiced yesterday, with my door closed lest I raise the hair of my very proper landlady, speaking to an imaginary audience on this subject. I was discouraged at the sound of my own voice; it is too soft, too childish, too unsure. I must remedy this! Finding it easier to write, and with my head full of the distressing subject, I put some of my thoughts into a letter to my sister Marian.

"I don't know if I've ever told you how deep this matter of licentiousness has gradually sunk into my soul, and that the determination to wage a war of extermination with it strengthens continually, and the hope of gaining power and experience to do it worthily is one of my strongest supports in action. So help me God, I will not be blind, indifferent, or stupid in relation to this matter, as are most women."

Nor will I!

And now at last January has come round again and it is time for graduation. I have taken my examinations and have passed them all creditably, I think. Brother Howard is coming to share the Great Day with me.

On January 23, 1849, Howard wrote to our family from my room in Geneva. He has shown me the letter, and I quote parts of it here.

BELOVED RELATIONS,—The important crisis is past, the great occasion over, the object of so much and so justifiable anticipation has been attained, and proud as I always feel of the Blackwells, my familism never seemed to me so reasonable and so perfectly a matter of course as it did this morning. . . . At ten o'clock A.M. the students met at the college and marched in procession. . . . Dr. Webster was very anxious that Elizabeth should march in procession, and sent down two messages to that effect; but E. very properly refused. About half-past ten o'clock Elizabeth and I walked up to the church—she was very nicely dressed in her black brocaded silk gown, black silk stockings, etc. As we ascended the college steps Dr. Webster met Eliz. and again urged the request, whereupon she told him peremptorily that "it wouldn't be ladylike." "Wouldn't it indeed? Why no, I forgot —I suppose it wouldn't," said the little Doctor, evidently struck for the first time with the idea. . . . We found the church, galleries and all, *crowded with ladies* . . . and of course when we came in there was a general stir and murmur, and everybody turned to look at us. When the procession entered, Mr. Field, a very pleasant, gentlemanly fellow-graduate, offered Elizabeth his arm, and all the class took their seats together in front of the stage. . . . The diplomas were conferred . . . Elizabeth was left to the last and called up alone. The President, taking off his hat, rose, and addressing her in the same formula, substituting Domina for Domine, presented her the diploma, whereupon our Sis, who had walked up and stood before him with much dignity, bowed and half

turned to retire, but suddenly turning back replied, "Sir, I thank you; by the help of the Most
High it shall be the effort of my life to shed honour
upon your diploma," whereupon she bowed, and
the President bowed, the audience gave manifesta-
tions of applause . . . and our Sis descending the
steps, took her seat with her fellow-physicians in
front. Now walks up into the pulpit Professor
Lee . . . and commences his address to the graduates. At the close . . . he passed a most gratifying
and enthusiastic encomium on the result of the
experiment in the case of Eliz. He pronounced
her the *leader* of her class, and said that by her
ladylike and dignified deportment she had proved
that the strongest intellect and nerve and the most
untiring perseverance were compatible with the
softest attributes of feminine delicacy and grace,
etc., to which all the students manifest by decided attempts at applause their entire concur-
rence. . . . As we walked out of the church we
found that almost all the ladies had stopped outside, and as we appeared, opened their ranks and
let us pass, regarding E. with very friendly coun-
tenances.

And so they did. It was gratifying and heartening,
but it was also amusing. I have come to realize that far
more notice than I thought—or ever hoped for—has
been taken of the fact that for the first time a woman
has been admitted to a complete medical education, and
has full equality in the privileges and responsibilities
of the profession. One newspaper remarked: "A very
notable event of the year 1848 was the appearance at

the medical lectures of a young woman student named Blackwell. She is a pretty little speciman of the feminine gender, said the Boston Medical Journal, reporting her age as twenty-six. She comes into class with great composure, takes off her bonnet and puts it under the seat, exposing a fine phrenology. The effect on the class has been good, and great decorum is observed while she is present. The sprightly Baltimore Sun remarked that she should confine her practice, when admitted, to diseases of the heart."

At the time that appeared I was a little put out, resenting the humorous tone. However, after reading some verses in the British publication, *Punch*, I see I must get used to a certain levity in regard to my new position. The magazine had this to say:

AN M.D. IN A GOWN

Not always is the warrior male,
Nor masculine the sailor;
We all know Zaragossa's tale,
We've all heard "Billy Taylor";
But far a nobler heroine, she
Who won the palm of knowledge,
And took a Medical Degree
By study at her College.

They talk about the gentler sex
Mankind in sickness tending,
And o'er the patient's couch their necks
Solicitously bending;
But what avails solicitude

In fever or in phthisic,
If lovely woman's not imbued
With one idea of physic?

Young ladies all, of every clime,
Especially of Britain,
Who wholly occupy your time
In novels or in knitting,
Whose highest skill is but to play,
Sing, dance, or French to clack well,
Reflect on the example, pray,
Of excellent Miss Blackwell!

Think, if you had a brother ill,
A husband, or a lover,
And could prescribe the draught or pill
Whereby he might recover;
How much more useful this would be,
Oh, sister, wife, or daughter!
Than merely handing him beef-tea,
Gruel, or toast-and-water.

Ye bachelors about to wed
In youth's unthinking hey-day,
Who look upon a furnish'd head
As horrid for a lady,
Who'd call a female doctor "blue";
You'd spare your sneers, I rather
Think, my young fellows, if you knew
What physic costs a father!

How much more blest were married life
To men of small condition
If every one could have his wife

For family physician;
His nursery kept from ailments free,
By proper regulation,
And for advice his only fee
A thankful salutation.

For Doctrix Blackwell—that's the way
To dub in rightful gender—
In her profession, ever may
Prosperity attend her!
"Punch" a gold-handled parasol
Suggests for presentation
To one so well deserving all
Esteem and admiration.

However, even with so much public notice of what is coming to be called my "achievement," I know that only the first step has been taken. I must have much more practical experience before I can consider the serious business of setting myself up as "Dr. Blackwell," ready for patients. An invitation has come from one of our Blackwell cousins, who is currently visiting America, to return with him to England and spend some time in European study before engaging in practice in this country. I have accepted this offer joyfully and will leave in April, but in the meantime I shall spend some time with my family. It may be years before I see them all again!

8 ⤲ *La Maternité*

⤲The voyage was hideous! I have always been prone to seasickness, but this trip was by far the worst. I recalled a remedy for the ailment that came from one of my uncles, but the very thought of it was more than I could bear.

"Swallow half a pint of sea water to clear the stomach," Uncle Browne used to say, "then take a cup of warm chocolate to coat it. This will come up. Then pour down a cup of scalding hot tea and stay well for the rest of the voyage."

I could not possibly have managed it!

But now it is wonderful to be back in England! I did not realize how much I remembered of it, nor how much I had missed it. I was only eleven when we sailed to America, but many memories have stayed fresh in my mind. The beautiful spring flowers, primroses and cowslips, seemed like old friends when I saw them again; the sweet voice of the nightingale was familiar and precious. I could spend days just wandering round the English countryside, or prowling the dear, dingy, smoky streets of London, but I must make some definite start at finding a place in which to further my education.

With various introductions in hand to British physicians, I have been visiting one hospital after another, talking to doctors, watching operations, observing methods of treatment, and in every case being met with

professional courtesy. I have been entertained at dinners and social evenings, I have even discovered that
iced champagne is a most delightful drink!

Many of these English doctors urge me to pursue my
studies in Paris. I hear nothing here of it being the
sinful and immoral city that I was once told it was,
only that it is the best place for medical training. Since
apparently there is no longer any need for me to give
up petticoats for trousers in order to work in Paris, I
have determined to go.

In any case I shall have family support against whatever mysterious "sins" I may encounter, since my sister
Anna is on her way back there as a foreign correspondent for American newspapers. So, although I
have very little money and very few introductions of
value, I will have someone of my own, and I can speak
the language. If Paris is where the most advanced
medical training can be found, I am off to Paris, immoral city or no!

What a strange crusade I seem to have engaged in!

Did I say I could speak the language? Good heavens! How different this rushing spate of words sounds
from the carefully measured phrases I was taught! My
first night in Paris I spent in a hotel. The charge
seemed exorbitant, but I was unable to argue with the
manager because of my sudden self-consciousness in
using French, so I accepted, and then could barely
wait until morning to get out and look for lodgings.

With the aid of a Mr. Doherty, a family acquaint-

ance whose address I had, I was able to find a pleasant little room with bedroom attached, very clean,
and at a moderate rent. My landlady is a delightful
woman, and we have shared a few walking trips about
the city while she points out places I should know,
and I take advantage of the chance to make myself
more fluent in the language. I have ordered myself a
new bonnet, choosing plain gray silk, though I was
assured again and again that "nobody wears that
color."

Nobody but the willful Dr. Blackwell, perhaps.

It was so good to see my sister Anna again! I must
have been particularly demonstrative in my welcome,
because she laughed at me.

"You are just glad to have someone with whom you
can speak English," she said.

I couldn't deny that, but, in addition, Anna, who is
the most outgoing member of our family, has a way
of making herself quite at home wherever she is, and
she has given me some much-needed confidence. She
has lived in Paris before, and took charge immediately, finding new quarters for us to share, introduc-
ing me to the many people she seems to know, insist-
ing that I accompany her to all sorts of social gatherings. Her casual introduction of me as "my sister, Dr.
Elizabeth Blackwell," has raised a number of eye-
brows, but I have been easily accepted. The French,
perhaps, are a bit less conventional than the English,
though I have yet to glimpse any "sinful immorality."

As my command of French has increased I have

dared to visit the few medical men to whom I had introductory letters, and these few have very kindly arranged meetings for me with others. After weeks of talking, listening, watching, observing, and learning my way around, I have decided to enter La Maternité hospital for training in obstetrics, and the entrance has been arranged. I find I now have three objectives. The first, to work at La Maternité, which seems assured. The second, to learn all there is to learn about obstetrics, and that, certainly, is my own responsibility. The third—loftiest of all—to become a surgeon! For that ambition I can only work and wait.

La Maternité is a great state institution where many young women are sent from all over France to be trained as midwives, or *"sage-femmes."* I have already learned that French doctors show beautiful manners toward a female physician, but have little faith in her ability or seriousness of purpose. Therefore, when I enter La Maternité it will be with a rather ambiguous status. Title I will have, but not the privileges which go with it.

Anna regards this with doubt. "You should insist on treatment in keeping with your position, Elizabeth," she told me.

"My position does not yet permit me to dictate terms, Anna. That may come, but the experience must come first. No, I am determined to work at La Maternité, whatever the conditions are, so you must just resign yourself to having your sister classed as a midwife."

Anna pursed her lips with distaste, but said no more. The date has been set for June 30. It draws close.

A few days after my arrival at La Maternité I wrote to my mother.

> DEAR MOTHER,—I have now entered a strange phase of my life, which I must try and describe, that you may imagine me running about in my great white apron, in which respectable article of apparel I expect to figure for the next three months. I had a good many obstacles to encounter from my ignorance of French customs; and the physicians of Paris . . . are determined not to grant the slightest favour to a feminine M.D. I could not obtain from any persons . . . the smallest modification to suit the very different status with which I enter from the young French *"sage-femmes"*. . . . I find now that nothing would have been easier than to have given me a little room to myself, permission to go out occasionally, and similar favours . . . but everything was obstinately refused, and I was only too glad to enter as a young, ignorant French girl. On June 30 I drove down with Anna to the hospital. A high stone wall, with the tops of buildings peeping above, extends nearly the whole length of a little street. A very small door led into a dark little entrance . . . the ceiling is very low, the floor of brick . . . the most uninteresting room you can possibly conceive. . . . Madame Blockel, the superintendent . . . took me into the infirmary and said I must sleep there. . . . My trunk was brought up, my bed pointed out,

a little lamp placed on the table, and I was left alone. . . . Presently Madame Charrier (the *sage-femme* in chief) entered . . . to know if I would pass the night in the *salle d'accouchements* [delivery room]. . . . Of course I expressed the utmost willingness. . . . A large apron of coarse towelling was given me, with the injunction not to lose it, or I should have to pay three francs. The room where the children are born is a large upper room, rather dimly lighted, beds all round, a fire on the hearth, cupboards full of linen in the corners, heaps of shining copper and tin utensils, several rush-bottomed chairs and wooden tables, and in the centre a large wooden stand with sides, on which the little newcomers, tightly swathed and ticketed, are ranged side by side. In the course of the night we had the pleasure of arranging eight in this way. . . . It was really very droll. Each little shapeless red visage peeped out from under a coarse peaked cap, on the front of which was a large label with the name and sex: a black serge jacket with a white handkerchief pinned across, and a small blanket tightly folded round the rest of the body, completed the appearance of the little mummy.

And how many of those "little mummies" I shall probably see before I leave here!

I am impressed by the cheerfulness and high spirits of the students, *"les élèves,"* who are just as gay in the middle of the night as on a sunny morning. How they do chatter! I have, happily, been moved out of the infirmary and into a dormitory where there are sixteen beds, and the room is rarely quiet. There are often sudden raging quarrels between students when voices climb high and I wait in dread of physical violence, but in a few moments it is all over and forgiven.

Their vitality is unbounded! A favorite amusement involves our iron bedsteads, which are on rollers. Getting together, they push one bed at the beginning of the long row, so that all the beds go clanging in an unbelievable pandemonium, sliding across the slippery tile floor. Or one student will climb onto a bed while others send it hurtling to the other end of the room, and all the while the girls are shouting, laughing, singing, or joking at the tops of their not inconsiderable lungs. The noise is deafening, and I found it difficult at first to control my temper, but no one asked me to be here, and I suppose their youthful spirits must have some freedom. They are so *young!* In all honesty, I don't think I was ever as young as they. Or did I never have the chance to be?

There is certainly no time during the day to wonder about such things. I am up at half-past five every morning unless I have worked the night before, dress and then bustle off to care for the few patients assigned to me. When I have inquired about their condition, washed and made them comfortable, it is quarter after six, and Madame Charrier makes her rounds. I join her entourage and listen as each *élève* gives a short report on the patient under her care. By now it is seven o'clock. Quickly I make my bed, fetch my coffee and drink it hastily with the loaf of long bread which is given us each day; then back to see more patients when they are visited by Dr. Girardin, the chief physician, and M. Hippolyte Blot, a young, handsome, and very dignified intern.

The rest of the day is taken up with lectures, which I attend to increase my fluency in French, more visits to special cases which interest me, a meal at noon and another at six in the evening. The food is nourishing and good, and I am learning to take a little wine with meals, which everyone advises me to do. Before each meal we stand around the tables, each of which seats twelve, and a grace is said with such rapidity that I am still unable to make out the words. The sign of the cross is made with wonderful quick dexterity, and then everyone pulls out her chair and starts to eat, consuming her plateful with astonishing speed. At the end of the meal another prayer rocket is sent up and everyone crowds out into the hall, carrying whatever tidbits they have been able to find in order to sustain themselves later.

In whatever little time remains I write my family or read a bit; then bathe and climb into my high bed at the earliest hour possible. The work excites me, I sleep dreamlessly all night, and am ready to resume my schedule in the morning. Hard work is an excellent tonic!

I have seen quite a bit of M. Blot, the young intern. He directs the vaccination of the babies, which takes place every Tuesday, and I sit quietly beside him, "observing." If I address a question to him he colors deeply, avoiding my eyes, and running his hand through his thick dark hair in a very un-Frenchman-like manner. I find myself wondering whether my questions merely annoy him, or whether—possibly—he finds me somewhat attractive and wishes to hide it. He is a *very* handsome man!

M. Blot is becoming quite human! I begin to think that his formal stiffness may be a deliberate effort to protect his professional dignity from the feminine flutterings that accompany his progress through the hospital. Both the students and the patients preen and simper outrageously whenever his dark saturnine face appears in a doorway. The taking of a pulse is a moment of exquisite pleasure, and his hand placed on a forehead to test for fever seems enough to raise the fever itself.

And I? I certainly hope I do not preen or simper, but I cannot deny a very feminine flutter when he asked me recently to give him some lessons in English. We have shared several sessions now, and I find myelf looking forward intensely to each one. How gratifying it is to a woman's vanity to see admiration in the eyes of a man! I find myself using a mirror more than I have in months, and there are times when I feel much more woman than doctor! Oh, Elizabeth, how vulnerable you are!

However, in spite of what I may read in Hippolyte Blot's eyes, or *think* I read, our conversation is never more than friendly, but that friendliness has removed his barriers of extreme dignity when we are together.

He now even indulges in some gentle teasing on such subjects as my concern with cleanliness and sanitation, which he considers female rather than medical.

Just a day or so ago he showed me a new instrument he has, a stethoscope, and allowed me to experiment with it. It is a thin black wooden tube, flared like a horn at one end, and with a smaller flange at the other. By holding the wider end against a patient's chest or back, and placing one's ear at the opposite flange, all the respiratory sounds become much clearer.

"Very modern and scientific, eh?" M. Blot said with one of his rare smiles. "And more delicate! A doctor need no longer embarrass his female patients by placing his ear on her—ah—chest."

I thought of the many patients who are admitted in a distressingly unwashed, ripe-odored state, and laughed.

"And more sanitary, M. Blot. Much, much more sanitary!"

But not everything is delicate, or even sanitary. I am often appalled at what I see in the *salle d'accouchements*. About the only women who experience no trouble are those who would have been perfectly capable of delivering their babies themselves in a brief interval between breakfast and lunch. A totally normal birth proceeds with no untoward incident and the healthy, screaming baby is laid beside his healthy, smiling mother. But for every one of these there are a dozen prolonged labors, misuses of forceps, rough handling by the students, inhumane examinations, and—often—death of both mother and child.

The incidence of puerperal fever following childbirth is distressingly high. M. Blot has told me that every effort is being made to discover the cause of it, not only in La Maternité, but in many hospitals in other countries as well.

"We have done autopsies on these victims," he told me, "hoping to find some clue as to the cause of the disease. We have then—while our minds were still fresh with what we had seen in the mortuary—gone directly to the patients and examined them carefully, searching for some link—some hint. But to no avail."

I tried to make my voice casual. "You washed before visiting the patients? After you had left the mortuary?"

"Washed? Certainly not. We wasted no time in washing. It was more important that we examine the patients immediately."

I hesitated, but our new friendliness allowed me to speak out bravely. "M. Blot, I have read of some study done by a man named Semmelweis, in Vienna, I believe. He has a theory that the cause of the disease may lie in the stench—the miasma—that comes from the corpses. He advocates the careful washing of hands before any living body is examined."

M. Blot smiled tolerantly. "Doctors would never

get their work done if they stopped a dozen times a day to wash their hands," he said. "And in cold weather such frequent washing could lead to chilblains, which would be very difficult for a surgeon. No, *chére* Dr. Blackwell, there can be nothing in such a theory. I am as concerned as you with finding the cause of puerperal fever, but I think you lay too much stress on all this washing and cleaning. I can see no connection."

I suppose he is correct, and he knows far more of such things than I. But I cannot rid myself of the belief that hygiene and sanitation play an important part in medicine. Unfortunately, no one agrees with me.

It was **M.** Blot who asked me to stay six months rather than the three I had planned. I agreed. I wonder whether I should have said "Yes" so happily if it had been someone else who asked me. I tell myself it is not the man, but the training; not being where Hippolyte Blot is, but being where I can learn more of my profession. That is what I *tell* myself!

In any event, I am gaining a certain ability and knowledge concerning obstetrics, as I promised myself I would, so two of my earlier objectives are now being achieved. My desire to become a surgeon—the first woman surgeon—grows stronger all the time.

M. Blot intends to further his study of surgery also. Oh, *Elizabeth!*

9 ∾ *The Accident*

∾ On Sunday, November 4, 1849, in the early dark hours of the morning, I was syringing the eye of one of my tiny patients who had purulent ophthalmia, a dreaded disease, and one result of syphilis in the mother. Crying, the baby jerked his head, and some of the water spurted back from his eye to mine. All that day my own eye felt as though there were a grain of sand in it, and by night it was much swollen. In the morning the lids were firmly closed, stuck together by the suppuration.

I went to the infirmary where M. Blot examined my eye carefully and so gently, and I did not need him to tell me that it was infected with the same disease the baby had. He tried to be encouraging and optimistic, saying that everything depended on the early treatment, and that I was to get myself to bed promptly, and that he would give up the next few days entirely to me. Only a short while ago I would have been thrilled at such evidence of his care and interest, but at that moment I was too wretched to say anything.

I sent off word to my sister Anna, and then gave myself up to the active treatment. My eyelids were cauterized; leeches—repulsive things!—were applied to my temples; cold compresses, or ointment of belladonna, or opium were rubbed on my forehead. I was given purgatives, footbaths, and for a diet nothing but broth. Every hour the eye was syringed, and nothing could have brought home to me more strongly the danger of the ailment than to realize how carefully this syringing was done. M. Blot was taking no chances of becoming infected as I had.

Anna came to see me that first evening, ready to sympathize with the "inflamed eye" I had informed her of. She spoke to me at my bedside, took my hand, and then moved rapidly away and I could hear her weeping. What a sinister fright I must have looked!

For the next several days this went on. The infirmary was kept profoundly quiet, and I could barely hear the hushed whispers of the young students as they gathered at the door to ask about me. Through the intense pain I realized that day and night M. Blot seemed to be there. I have no notion when he may have slept. Anna came and went, trying not to let me sense her fears, but I was a doctor. I knew far better than she how gloomy the prognosis was. I had seen for myself how the daylight gradually faded as M. Blot bent over me, and with an exquisite delicacy of touch removed the film that had formed over the pupil of my left eye. I could see him for a moment clearly, his handsome face clouded with worry, and then the sight vanished and the eye was left in darkness.

For three weeks I lay in bed with both eyes closed. Then at last the right began to open gradually, and I could get up and manage to do a few things for myself, even with very limited sight. I brushed and braided my hair, more by touch as all women do, and when M. Blot came in to see me he smoothed it gently.

"Beautiful!" he said. "How is it that fingers without eyes can make anything so perfectly regular?"

"Fingers without eyes can do many things," I told him. "But they are not the things a surgeon must do."

He put his hand over mine. "Surgery is not the only important field of medicine," he pointed out, "and perhaps, in time, the sight will come back to the eye—"

I tried to smile. "You must never lie to your doctor," I reminded him. "A one-eyed surgeon would be of little use. But you are right, there are other things."

He stood gazing at me as though he wanted to say much more, but then he laid his hand on my shoulder, pressed it, and quietly left the room. I wanted to cry after him, "Don't go! Don't leave me! I'm afraid!" But the words died in my throat, and I could not call him back.

A few days later I dressed for the first time, finding myself surprisingly weak after so long in bed. Anna had come for me, and—bandaged and veiled—I was led to the door and then guided into the carriage. As many of the *élèves* as could be there crowded in the doorway waving, and behind them I glimpsed the tall dark form of Hippolyte Blot. He raised his hand—almost like a benediction. It was the last thing I saw as we drove away from La Maternité.

I must have been even weaker than I thought, for

all that evening in Anna's rooms I alternated between foolish laughter and childish tears.

Without reason I found myself still hoping that sight would be restored to my left eye. My right eye, the "good" one, was growing stronger daily, but all immediate thoughts of anatomical or surgical work had to be put aside, and even reading was out of the question. As my strength returned I attended a few medical lectures, and, by invitation, some clinic sessions at the famous hospital Hôtel-Dieu, but these were not sufficient to keep me occupied, either mentally or physically. In June I resolved to go to an establishment in Grafenberg, Prussia, run by a gentleman named Priessnitz, who had achieved some remarkable water cures.

It was a beautiful spot, surrounded by mountains and thickly wooded, with air as clear and invigorating as the iced champagne I had learned to like so much. There were many patients, all ladies and gentlemen, even including some members of the nobility, and we joined together in living the simplest life imaginable. The course of treatment consisted of numerous baths of every variety—plunge baths, sitz baths, half-baths, plus glasses and glasses of the particular health-giving water. There were long walks through the woods and over the mountains, and meals made largely of bread, butter, milk and the delicious little Alpine strawberries.

After some weeks I rejoiced in returning health! I felt so well that all thought of sickness seemed imagined, and my spirits soared. But this euphoria did not last. The constant outdoor life and long rambles over the Bohemian countryside proved too stimulating to my still sensitive eye, and a violent attack of inflammation sent me fumbling back to Paris where I placed myself under the care of the famous oculist, Desmarres. No one could have been kinder, more skillful nor more generous with his time and attention, but the damage had been done, and in order to save my right eye from infection, the left one had to be removed.

I say that so simply! My *eye*—a part of myself—my means of looking upon the world—*my eye!* To be less than whole, to be disfigured—for I have seen glass eyes, shining, fixed, unmoving, expressionless—I am a woman! And still reasonably young, not yet thirty. Never a beauty, certainly, but not unattractive! I don't *want* to be hideous!

I even knew how the operation would be done, with the eyelid stretched to a terrible wideness, while skillful fingers clipped and cut. I felt sickened at the thought, and nearly wild with despair. The memory of that horrible bullock's eye kept filling my mind—that eye which was shown me by a professor during my early school years. I have never forgotten it, and now it was like a recurring nightmare. In my terror I would try to fasten my thoughts on to something else, but that was useless. From thinking of myself as a woman, I would think of myself as a doctor. A *doctor* with a glass eye! Never a surgeon now, just a doctor. And how good a doctor? Who trusts a one-eyed doctor?

I think I have never been so in need of someone to cling to. If Hippolyte Blot had appeared in my room I would have thrown myself into his arms in torrents of self-pitying tears. But he did not, and my pride would not let me send him any word.

Anna was in almost a worse state than I, and with her I could not voice my own anguish. If I once allowed a crack to appear in my control, I knew my fear, my disgust, my deep, deep hurt would pour forth, drowning me and all those who cared for me.

So Dr. Elizabeth Blackwell, her whole being aching with unshed tears, discussed the situation calmly with her surgeon, the decision was made, and the operation was performed. In time I was released from the hospital.

My main question was, what am I being released *to*?

10 ❧ *England*

❧ As so often happens, the answer has come. One of my many cousins, Kenyon Blackwell, who lives in England, has somehow managed to have me invited to enter the great St. Bartholomew's Hospital in London, where I shall be allowed to study quite freely.

Coming at this particular time it seems like a gift from heaven! I have left Anna in Paris, found myself lodgings in a blessedly quiet set of houses known as Thavies Inn, and every morning I trot off to the hospital to spend a full and stimulating day.

For a while after the operation I wanted nothing more than to hide myself from everyone, but my honesty and my mirror have at last combined to tell me that I look little different than before. I do not delude myself into thinking that a careful observer will not notice immediately that Dr. Blackwell has a very glassy stare in her left eye, but I am still alive, the world is still here, and there is work that I can do. Therefore, I am making friends among the doctors (and what a relief to be able to speak English all the time!) and have even attended some social gatherings. The gentlemen all seem more friendly than their ladies, and I understand that I am still regarded by many people as "that strange creature, the lady doctor."

But some of the women I have met are so much in accord with what I have done, and support women's rights so strongly, they cannot seem to do enough for me. I was sitting one afternoon in my bare lodging-house drawing room—bare because I never seem to have even a few extra pennies for luxuries—when there was a knock on my door, and I admitted three delightful young ladies, a Miss Bessie Parkes, and two sisters, the Misses Leigh Smith. In a very short time they seem to have taken charge of part of my life, and what a change they have made! They have hung the walls of my rooms with paintings which they change according to their whims, surrounded me with fresh flowers cut from their gardens, and welcomed me into their family circles with the warmest hospitality. They have taken me to parties, concerts, lectures, art exhibitions, and the theater until I seem to be living in a social whirl of activities that excite me.

They have introduced me to all manner of interesting people I had never hoped to meet, such as the unconventional but brilliant Miss Mary Ann Evans, who writes novels under the name of George Eliot; the famed poet and painter, Dante Gabriel Rossetti, who always surprises me by being very English in spite of his name; the rebellious artist and writer, John Ruskin; Lady Noel Byron, widow of the tragic poet; and Fanny Kemble, that entrancing actress whose voice can thrill one's heart.

I have little to say to these talented people, and I feel shy in their presence, but I listen to their revolutionary views on social and artistic matters and am the richer for knowing them. Another young woman I have met is much more my own sort of person, and I count her as a friend. Her name is Florence Nightingale.

Miss Nightingale lives with her parents in a beautiful large home, but chafes constantly against the restrictions that prevent her from doing what she calls "something worthwhile" in the world. The medical profession interests her deeply, though she claims she would be content as a nurse. This desire receives no sympathy from her parents. I visited her at Embley Park one spring weekend. She showed me round the very handsome house, and then we went outside for a walk through the beautiful grounds. As we wandered across the lawn in front of the great drawing room she said, "Do you know what I always think when I look at that row of windows?"

"Tell me," I said.

"I think how I should turn it into a hospital ward, and just how I should place the beds."

I laughed. "We should work together," I said lightly. "You supply the hospital and be the nurse in charge, and I shall be the one-eyed lady physician. What a boon we would be!"

Florence stopped and looked at me. "I am quite serious, Elizabeth," she said. "I should like nothing better than working with you."

Whether this will ever come to pass I cannot say, but Florence and I agree on many things to do with medicine, such as the importance of sanitation and personal hygiene. This seems to both of us the foundation of health, and the lack of it—which is so common —the greatest cause of disease.

I am quite sure that this must be one of the happiest periods of my life! To have won my medical degree; to be quite accepted here in England as a physician; to have the chance to study and work in a modern, well-equipped hospital; to have numerous friends with whom I can enjoy recreation and social activities —there is little more I could ask. Except my eye. But better not to think of that.

I have seen all sorts of wonderful sights, including the opening of the Great Industrial Exhibition. I had watched the building as it rose rapidly in Hyde Park, thinking all the while that the iron framework, which appeared so delicate when combined with the enormous glass sides, looked too fragile to support the building, but I attended the opening celebration and saw how wrong I was.

With thanks to another cousin, Samuel Blackwell, who was an exhibitor, I was there on May 1 of this year, 1851, and I shall never forget the occasion. The vast structure, resplendent with the products of the whole world; the air beating with voices and music and laughter; and then the entrance of Queen Victoria, holding Prince Albert's arm, with the young Prince of Wales on one side and the Princess Royal on the other, and followed by a long train of nobility. Slowly they toured the building and declared it open, and I was deeply moved by the pride and love that illuminated the queen's face as she looked at her husband and rejoiced in his accomplishment. The experience was unforgettable.

But all this pleasant, social living does not change

the fact that I am first and foremost a doctor, and it is as a doctor that I must plan my life. I cannot remain a student forever, although I think there would always be something new to learn in this ever-growing field of medicine. I have, of necessity, given up the dream of becoming a surgeon.

Now my hopes and ambitions are centered on a greater and better education for women, not in *opposition* to men, but in order to become contributive, responsible, informed members of society, which—at the moment—they are not.

The ways in which the average woman may support herself are circumscribed by men. Women may teach, they may nurse, they may serve as domestic servants, they may labor in factories for a pittance and under deplorable conditions, they may become prostitutes. I say the "average" woman, because specifically talented women can, of course, work in a wider field, such as the theater, music, painting, or literature.

Since my own profession is medicine, it would seem to follow that whatever effort I may expend in bettering the female lot should be in this area. If I could be instrumental in establishing the best medical training for women it would be one more step forward, and this, I think, will now be my goal.

I have seriously considered remaining in England, which I still feel is my real home, and going into practice here, but there are certain things against it. Most importantly, I seem always to be extremely poor, with no capital to fall back on, and a great horror of running into debt. My friends here are not of the sort I would go to for financial aid, and my family is not here to assist me. In addition, that same dear family is looking forward to my return, and I feel I cannot remain away any longer.

I have therefore determined to return to New York, open a practice, and work toward better and more available medical training for women. I have some very definite ideas on this training, learned from my own experience, and what I have heard from other doctors. We all accept the present method of teaching, but I am sure there must be better ways.

Why should students not have access to hospitals and be given an opportunity to observe the diseases about which they study? Textbooks and lectures are necessary, but must virtually all actual experience wait until after graduation? It is only rarely that a medical school works closely with a hospital—I think it should be common practice.

After the accident to my eye at La Maternité, and when I was with Anna in Paris, trying desperately to fill my time, I had the good fortune to be allowed to do some dissecting at *L'École des Beaux-Arts*. There was no one with me to instruct me, and with only one good eye I may have overlooked or not recognized some things. On one occasion I was literally smuggled into the dead-house of *L'Hôpital La Charité* by a student I had hired to drill me in anatomy (for the Parisian training does give students more opportunities than British or American), and there I "operated" on a cadaver. But these were among the few chances I had to work with my own hands on a corpse. Should this not be done in school? How much can one learn from watching and listening and reading? Should not practical experimentation, safely and professionally arranged, start early in medical training? As for that, should there not be more years of training, to eliminate the need for so much study after graduation? Above all, should not hygiene and sanitation be stressed as all-important to health?

In any event, my head is now filled with plans for returning to New York and working toward a medical training school for women that will incorporate these ideas. It will be painful to leave the many friends and opportunities I have found in England, but I learned long ago that the life I chose requires much self-denial. I trust I shall always be strong enough to live within the restrictions.

11 ❦ *New York*

❦ Oh, the futility of the dreams we dream! Yet if we did not have those dreams to sustain us we might all give up in despair much earlier in our efforts.

I am in New York, and except for my family I cannot say New York has been eager to greet me. It was

wonderful to see Mother, serene, reassuring, and un-
surprised, as always, by anything her headstrong
daughter might do. And Marian, looking far too frail
in a wide-hooped blue gown—I think she is not as
well as she should be—and dear Ellen, bustling about
and taking care of all the baggage while the rest of us
stood talking. There has been much building in the
city, and everything seems closer together than when
I saw it last, but the spire of Trinity Church is still
the beacon of the waterfront, and the docks seemed
to surge with activity and excitement.

Mother had taken temporary rooms, and I know she
was hoping I would announce my intention of returning to Cincinnati with them, but I could not. What I
must do, I must try to do here in New York. And I can
see already that it is not going to be easy.

I spent days walking the streets in search of rooms
in which to set up my practice, but I had only to mention my profession and doors were slammed in my
face. The moment I introduce myself as "Dr. Blackwell" I am suspected of being a member of one of the
many "quack" cults that are prevalent—mesmerism,
clairvoyance, spiritualism, or—worse yet—an abortion-
ist, since they have been for years the only women to
use the title "Doctor." I have dressed modestly and
carried myself with dignity, but I have not been able
to overcome the general prejudices.

At last, one mild September morning, I succeeded
in renting an entire floor of a house on University

Place. The rent was exorbitant, and I had to supply all furnishings myself, thus cutting into my scant savings in a terrifying way, but at least I was able to hang out my shingle and insert an announcement in the *New York Tribune* that "Dr. Elizabeth Blackwell has opened an office and is ready for patients."

Whether any patients were ready for Dr. Elizabeth Blackwell in those first weeks I never knew, since my landlady failed to deliver messages. I am sure she already regrets the greed that led her to rent me the rooms, for she indicates that no "lady" would live in a house marked with the shingle of a female doctor, and that she is accused of running a disrespectable house. I have not, however, offered to leave, and her appreciation of my considerable rent prevents her from asking me to go.

I have no desire to stand alone as a woman physician, so I took my American and English testimonials to one of New York's largest dispensaries and asked for a chance to work as assistant physician in the department for women and children. This was refused with dispatch and I was quite scornfully advised to start my own dispensary. I have sought permission to visit the women's wards of Bellevue Hospital, but that application did not even receive the dignity of a reply.

With no claims on my professional experience, I have spent half of each day waiting in my lonely consultation room, and the other half walking the fascinating city streets. After several such walks I realized

I was taking note of the many young girls and women I saw, and thinking of them in terms of medical health, mental growth, and emotional contentment.

I see them mincing along from shop to shop, tightly corseted, swathed in layers of clothing, their faces simpering and seeming to lack all vivacity. As a result, I sat down one afternoon, sole occupant of my office, and proceeded to write the outline of a lecture on the physical education of girls. This led to further thoughts and more complete writing, until now, in March 1852, I have set up a course of six lectures and bravely plan to deliver them in a basement Sunday-school room. I have no way of knowing whether there will be an audience, though I have placed an announcement in the *New York Times,* and I admit to qualms. But I *must* do something!

People came! Very few at first, and all ladies, but intelligent and open-minded. There was a constantly increasing number of members of the Society of Friends, which did not surprise me, as I have always found Quakers to be advanced and liberal in their thinking.

And what did I tell them, these brave, tolerant people? I told them of the stifling life of the contemporary city girl, her lack of exercise and mental stimulation, her (often) too early marriage as her only destiny, a marriage undertaken with total ignorance of the functions of her own body and the fundamentals of health. I pointed out the city's crowded living conditions, poor ventilation, excessive heating from stoves and fireplaces, the absence of parks or public squares and the disappearance of city gardens in which to exercise. I mentioned the trend toward unwholesome and over-rich food.

I suggested increased education, combined with physical activity, listing climbing, running, fencing, dancing, pantomime, riding, archery, and even wrestling as the means toward a light, fleet, healthy body. I urged young mothers to free their babies from tight swaddling clothes, and give them more sunshine and fewer expensive toys. I ventured that girls should feel that they had work to do in the world, and a greater purpose than an early marriage, undertaken solely from lack of any other objective.

And as the lectures progressed and I gained confidence from the increasing number of women who attended, I described fully the process of birth—which even many women who had produced several children did not understand—and argued that young people should have full and specific knowledge of their bodies. I even dared to say that the schools and colleges should offer practical study in these natural sciences, and should stress the importance of sanitation. And at last, with a feeling that I might well be cooking my own goose, I said firmly that while America might be advanced in matters of academic education for women, nowhere in the world were the physical needs of children so neglected and nowhere were young women so feeble.

And then, appalled by my own daring, I waited for the skies to fall. Instead, those blessed Quaker women are beginning to come to me as a doctor! The first was Mrs. Stacy B. Collins, who somehow importuned her husband, a printer and publisher, to engage me as their family physician, and to the Collins family I shall be forever indebted. For they opened the way to others, and now there is—if not a stream of patients—at least a slowly increasing trickle.

But there has been another and less happy result of those lectures. I have received threatening letters, always anonymous, accusing me of perverting the minds of innocent women. When I go into the street I am frequently jeered at, and often insulted. Sometimes women who recognize me hold back their skirts as they pass, just as they did in Geneva, and more times than I can count I have heard a female remark that, "I would rather *die* than have a woman doctor!" Someday I am afraid I shall forget all prudence and snap back, "If I had my way, madam, that would be your entire choice!"

And it is not only the ladies who feel so. Not long ago one of my few and precious patients, an elderly woman, contracted a severe case of pneumonia. There was a respected physician currently living in New York, whom I had known when my father was ill in Cincinnati. Thinking it would now be wise to consult with another doctor, I asked my acquaintance to meet me at the patient's house, which he did. He examined her carefully, and then went with me into the parlor, where he began to walk round the room in great agitation.

"A most extraordinary case," he said. "Such a one never happened to me before! I really do not know what to do!"

My heart plummeted. Had I somehow misread the symptoms? Was it something even worse than pneumonia?

"What is it?" I asked. "Not pneumonia?"

"Certainly it's pneumonia," he said impatiently. "You know that."

"I thought I did," I admitted, "but you seem so concerned. Are there complications?"

"Complications? Of course there are complications! The complications of consulting with a lady doctor. I am not at all sure it is proper, Elizabeth!"

I was so relieved I laughed. "Then let us not call it a consultation," I said. "Just a friendly talk between old acquaintances. Would that reassure you?"

At last he smiled. "Women like you, Elizabeth, can make life very difficult for men like me," he said. "I shall call it a consultation, which may make it easier for you to obtain advice in the future. But *why* did you have to enter the medical profession?"

I looked up at him. "Partly to prove that a woman could," I said. "And you see, Doctor, that a woman has."

Due to the kindness and interest of my Quaker friends and patients, I have taken two small steps forward. The series of lectures I gave has been published under the title, "The Laws of Life in reference to the Physical Education of Girls," and it has brought me several encouraging letters from other doctors.

In addition, after I had applied again to a New York hospital for a dispensary position, and had been told that "a lady doctor would not promote the harmonious working of the institution," I resolved to form an independent dispensary, and this, too, has been aided by these same good people, both financially and through their physical help.

I found a small room near Tompkins Square, and placed another newspaper announcement, saying that I would receive patients three afternoons a week, and that my purpose was to give poor women an opportunity to consult a physician of their own sex. Would that I had done it sooner! The area was the poorest sort of slum neighborhood. Parents with ten or twelve children were often living in no more than two rooms; refuse was usually thrown out of the windows to pile up in the filthy yards; babies were born and died in the rat-infested tenements. The majority of the people were immigrants, all of them were poor, and most of them ignorant of even the most basic elements of cleanliness and health. But they were *not* prejudiced against female physicians! Slightly suspicious perhaps, at first, of the very small, very feminine doctor, but so in need of assistance that they would have come to me had I been the Devil himself.

I had a twofold purpose at Tompkins Square: to

give medical counsel, and solid advice about sanitation. To say that the latter took immediate hold would be untrue. No matter how often I urged them to eliminate half the wrappings that bound the limbs of their babies, the infants would be just as tightly swaddled the next time I saw them. No matter how often I advocated sunshine and fresh air for their children, the children still played on the filthy tenement floors. But gradually, *so* gradually, I have been accepted as a doctor. As "their" Doctor. When they cannot come to me, I go to them, walking through areas that would send my family into a communal fainting fit if they knew. I have bound up knife wounds and applied medication to the results of physical beatings. I have delivered babies whose mothers were lying on stinking heaps of sacking or rags on the floor, and whose fathers—if they were, indeed, the fathers—were drunk and noisy and insulting.

I am out at all hours of the day and night, sometimes in these degraded slums that would terrify me if I allowed myself to think about it, and sometimes in the sedate, immaculate homes of my Quaker patients. In summer I work in rooms where the temperature stands far above 100°, and in winter I shiver in rooms where nothing more than crumpled newspaper in the windows helps to keep out the cold. But I am at last a practicing physician! What a long time it has taken me!

12 ∾ Emily

ᏜWhenever I think I may have blazed a trail for other women of ambition to follow, I discover again how little progress has been made. My younger sister, Emily—she who promised years ago that if I would become a doctor, she would too—has reached the firm decision to live up to those words.

Heaven knows I have not encouraged her! As much as I should like to see her graduated, and in successful practice, I know only too well the loneliness and hardship involved. But Emily does not seem to need encouragement, only practical assistance. Financially I can do nothing, but it may be possible for me to arrange some interviews for her. She has been staying with me for a while this summer, 1852, and has told me of the several attempts she has made to enter a medical school. Eleven, to be exact! In every case—and how well I know the bitter disappointment!—she has been refused, even by my own school, Geneva, which seems now to be regretting its one small, brave step toward feminine education.

"If I could do *something* in the way of study, Elizabeth," she said passionately. "Just so I could feel I was not wasting precious time!"

I bethought myself of Mr. Horace Greeley, the founder and editor of the *New York Tribune,* whom I met through some of my Quaker friends. Mr. Greeley is extremely outspoken in favor of rights and advancement for women, and it seemed he might be willing and able to help Emily. Together we went to see him, and I think Emily was a little awed by this tall, pale, sprawling man who always looks on the brink of total exhaustion. Mr. Greeley promised to speak to a Simeon Draper at Bellevue Hospital, and I took it upon myself to mention the matter to another doctor there, and before we knew it Emily was actually walking the wards of Bellevue, something that has been denied to me.

I knew precisely how she felt when she came home in the evenings to tell me of her day.

"They laugh at me, Elizabeth," she said heatedly. "The other students—no older than I, and knowing little more than I do, but just because they are men they think it comical to see me take a pulse!"

"And this is only the beginning, Emily," I reminded her. "You had better become used to it, because it will be a long time before that attitude changes."

As I had done, Emily went her way quietly, arousing as little attention as possible. When the syphilitic cases were exhibited to students, Emily stayed discreetly outside the amphitheater. Every morning found her in the apothecary's shop watching as the prescriptions were made up, and in her hours around the hospital she picked up a great deal of information. When, joyfully, word came that she had been accepted by Rush College in Chicago, we celebrated with a small party, attended by our sister, Marian, who is living with us, Emily, and me. I had had three paying patients that week and made twenty-five dollars. It was a happy occasion!

I suppose there are many people who would find it hard to believe how lonely I am, since all day I am surrounded by patients and their relatives, and in the evening, although Emily is back at school, I have my sister Marian. The fact is that being lonely and being alone are very different things. I am rarely alone, but I am often depressingly lonely.

Marian is making her home with me, supporting herself by her stories and articles, and I am, of course, glad to have her. But she has always been a moody, silent person, given to sudden short-lived enthusiasms and a number of minor ailments—half of which I think are imaginary—and we share few interests.

If I only had someone of my own! Not a sister or brother, but someone whose life would be close to mine, with whom I could share talk and laughter. A husband? I am thirty-one years old. A small, slight, pale woman blessed with good health and cursed with a glass eye. I have made a life for myself which I think I could not give up for any man. I have the capacity to love, heaven knows!—but I could never be dominated by a husband. Hippolyte Blot? I think of him sometimes—and wonder—but that is over and done with. It seems unlikely now that I shall ever marry. But how wonderful it would be to have a child! There, indeed, would be someone of my own! Unfortunately, to have a child one must (if one is to be considered a lady) also have a husband. Since the chances of a husband are dim, the chances of a child are even dimmer.

Perhaps if I left this house, where my rooms cost me far more than they are worth, and where the neighborhood in general still regards me as distasteful, things might be happier. I might pull myself out of this depression that comes from the spiteful gossip about me. I am a woman as well as a physician, and both sides of my nature are wounded by the malicious stories which abound. It is very hard, with no support but a high purpose, to live against every species of social opposition. I should like a little fun now and then. Life is altogether too sober!

Emily came back to stay with me after her first year at Rush College, and the moment she walked in I knew something was wrong.

"What is it?" I asked. "Tell me."

Emily untied her bonnet and slipped it off, smoothing her thick reddish hair. "I can't go back," she said.

"Can't? What do you mean, can't? Is it money?"

"No, I have the money. I saved my earnings, just as you did."

"Then—?"

"The State Medical Society has censured the college for admitting a woman. The doors have been closed to me."

I sat down heavily. "Oh, Emily! It is so *unfair!*"

"Unfair? Yes, I suppose it is. But we never expected anything else, did we, Elizabeth?"

"What will you do now?"

"Work with you in the dispensary this summer, if you will have me, and pull every string I know to find another school by fall."

"But it is such a disappointment to you!"

"Elizabeth," Emily said softly, "I am stronger than you. I have always been. Oh, I don't mean physically— for all your small size you have the constitution of an ox!—but things don't hurt me as much as they do you. The things people say, for example, or being shut out. You are far more sensitive than I, and you can't shrug off disapproval as I can. Don't worry about me, Elizabeth. I am going to be all right!"

And somehow I think she will. She has given me a little extra courage, too.

I have bought a house! It may have been a fool-hardy move, considering my always impecunious state, but at least no one can frown upon me in my own establishment! One of my Quaker friends lent me the purchasing price at a reasonable rate of interest, and I have rented most of the house to a family that takes boarders, keeping only necessary rooms for myself. To be wholly truthful, *my* rooms are in the attic and base-ment, but they are my own! The house is on Fifteenth Street, and though the new neighbors may continue to stare and whisper as the old ones did, at the very least I have my attic and basement to reign over without criticism.

Emily, Marian and I had been living in the new house just a very short time when I was summoned to the home of one of my patients, Mrs. Peter Schermerhorn, to deliver her child. It was a hot day and the air was damp and humid. I had been sleepless most of the preceding night, almost stifled by the heat in the attic bedroom, and I felt exhausted. When Emily offered to come with me to Mrs. Schermerhorn's, I was delighted.

"I may not be of much help," Emily said, "but I promise not to get in your way."

It was a long and arduous accouchement. The sun beat in through the windows until I pulled the heavy dark drapes across them, and then the room became unbearably hot. From the temperature and the effort of giving birth, my patient lay drenched with perspiration, and I could feel my petticoats and even my dress clinging to my damp skin. Only Emily remained crisp and cool in appearance, and a tower of strength. When the child finally arrived, healthy and welcome, and was laid beside his mother, I almost crawled down the stairs to the door. Emily put her arm around me.

"Poor Elizabeth," she said.

"Why do you say 'poor'?"

"Because you look so tiny, and tired, and hot, and pathetic. When I have my degree, Elizabeth, I am going to work with you. That is, if you will have me."

"Have you?" I turned quickly to face her. "Oh, Emily, there is no one I'd rather have!"

"Then that is settled," she said firmly. "You really need someone to look out for you."

It seemed a ridiculous statement, coming from my "little" sister, but the prospect of working together delights me. I only hope it comes to pass.

Emily is an astonishing person! True to her word, she "pulled every string" and the autumn found her admitted to the medical college of Western Reserve University in Cleveland. To say I admire her would be an understatement. She has been snubbed, buffeted, refused and disappointed as much as, if not more than, I, yet she manages to retain her good humor, her optimism, and her confidence. Mine has been shaken often, but I know of nothing to do except stumble along in my narrow channel. The dispensary stimulates me, for here I believe I am both needed and appreciated, though rarely paid. It is my Quaker patients who keep the roof over my head, and a modicum of food in my stomach.

Marian is still living with me, between occasional visits home to see our family, and her writing gives her a small income. She seems to grow more morose all the time, and her ills become more frequent. I prescribe for her as much as she will permit, but I think her dyspepsia and related ailments are her main interest, and she would not want to be rid of them.

But my life is so lonely! I know many people, but

few who can be counted as close friends. All my friends seem to have been made when I lived in England. Lady Byron, who still writes to me, and Florence Nightingale, who has somehow gained the courage to defy her parents (she says that I inspired her) and take up the study of nursing—how much I miss them! If only there were someone to *share* my life with! If I had ever conceived how alone I should be, I am not at all sure I would have chosen a medical career. A woman needs more.

13 ∿ *Kitty and Marie*

∿What a change has come into my life! I have adopted a daughter! The decision was by no means a sudden one. It seemed simply to be the logical solution to my loneliness, and my need for someone to love. Marian thought I had lost my senses.

"Adopt a *child?*" she said, as though I had mentioned adopting a Barbary ape. "Elizabeth! What would you do with a *child?*"

"Love it," I replied promptly. "Surely there must be a child who needs to give and receive love as much as I do."

"But a child would be noisy—"

"I hope so. This house is much too quiet."

"—and destructive—"

"Not necessarily."

"—demanding—"

"I should welcome a few demands made on me. I have much to give."

"—and we have so little money."

"We have enough to clothe and feed one small child."

"Oh, Elizabeth! Have you *thought* about this?"

"Constantly. For months. I am going to the emigrant depot at Randall's Island and find an orphan girl. Would you like to come with me?"

Marian sighed heavily, rolling her eyes to heaven for assistance, but she could not resist accompanying me. I believe she hoped she would still be able to convince me of my folly, but that was impossible. My mind was quite made up.

And how glad I am that I never changed it!

There seemed to be hundreds of children in the pauper nursery of the depot when Marian and I stepped off the ferry, all sorts of children. All ages, races, sizes and conditions. Some were bursting with health and good spirits, others sat quietly apart, looking peaked and spindly. There was one little girl, redhaired, slight, and small. I kept passing her and then finding myself looking for her again. I noticed that her eyes seemed to bother her, for they were constantly blinking, and her muscular coordination seemed weak. At last I stopped and spoke to her.

"What is your name?" I asked.

"Kitty Barry," she said. Her voice was sweet, with an unmistakable Irish lilt.

"How old are you, Kitty?"

"Seven, ma'am."

"You are small for seven," I said.

Kitty glanced up at me, and there was a sparkle of laughter in her blinking blue eyes. Beyond any doubt she was thinking that I was certainly more than seven, but not very much taller than she. Her humor delighted me, and I moved aside and spoke to Marian.

"That's the child I want."

"That scrawny little creature? Oh, Elizabeth! She doesn't look at all strong!"

"All the more reason," I said. "She needs me more than the others."

So Kitty has come to live with us. The house on Fifteenth Street—or at least our attic and basement— sounds with her laughter, her light voice, her quick footsteps. I find her beloved doll sitting in my chair, her building blocks under my desk, and her skipping rope looped over the hat rack, and it fills me with joy!

I have already begun to work with her in gymnastic exercises in order to strengthen her weak ankles and improve her coordination; I have started to teach her music and French and German, and to all of this she responds by blooming like a flower! She calls me "Doctor," and warms me with her genial, fun-loving Irish temperament. Even Marian admits taking pleasure in Kitty, and often spends a few pennies on some toy or treat for the child.

It is hard to imagine how I existed without her. I can barely wait for Emily to meet her, but Emily is now in Edinburgh, studying gynecology with Sir James Young Simpson. She was graduated from Western Reserve triumphantly, as I was sure she would be, and is gaining unmatchable experience from Sir James, not only in women's diseases, but also in the use of chloroform, especially in childbirth. Queen Victoria herself was his patient during a confinement, and expressed her delight with the anesthetic. This testimonial has, of course, aided his work enormously, and Emily is benefitting from it.

Perhaps Kitty is really a good-luck talisman for me. She was playing outside the house one morning recently, and suddenly came running in to say there was a young lady to see me.

"Who is she, Kitty? A patient?"

"I don't know, Doctor," she said. "She doesn't speak like you. It was hard to know what she was saying."

"Well, bring her in, Kitty. Bring her in."

A moment later a tall, strong-faced young woman stood in the doorway.

"Dr. Blackwell?" she asked. I nodded. "I am Marie Zakrzewska. My English—it is very small."

I smiled, and made a quick guess at her accent. "You speak German?"

With an expression of relief she nodded. "And you?"

And then, speaking German together, we sat for more than an hour, while I listened to her story. She was the descendent of a number of distinguished doctors, surgeons, and midwives, and had been appointed by Dr. Schmidt, head of the Berlin midwifery department, to act as chief midwife in the Royal Hospital. There she taught classes of more than one hundred and fifty women and about fifty men, proving herself most capable. When Dr. Schmidt died, Marie decided to come to New York, hoping to continue in the same work, but the German doctors she has talked to here all urged her to become a nurse. To support herself she had been embroidering tasseled caps for fifty cents to a dollar a day, until—in desperation—she went to the Home for the Friendless, where she was advised to come to me.

I was very impressed by her seriousness and her knowledge of obstetrics, and was immediately drawn to her. It was obvious that she should endeavor to get a medical degree, and after Emily's success at Western Reserve University I felt that school might be receptive to another female student. I suggested to Marie that she work with me in the dispensary, that I would help her to learn English, and then do what I could to get her admitted to Western Reserve. Her gratitude was almost embarrassing.

"I cannot believe you take so deep an interest in me," she said. "I have grown so accustomed to rebuffs—"

"As have I," I said.

"When I was told that you were a doctor—with a *degree*—I could not believe it! I expected to find an eccentric woman, perhaps even fearsome, who would carry on at great length about woman's position in the world. You rarely mention the subject."

"Not because I don't feel strongly about it. Only because 'carrying on' has never seemed to accomplish a great deal. I would rather strengthen woman's position by doing what I can to advance someone like you."

For a moment I feared Marie might weep, but she is not the weeping kind. Her lashes were a trifle damp, it's true, but after we had arranged for her to commence work at the dispensary, she rose, took my hand in her firm one, found no words, and walked quickly out.

A few moments later Kitty appeared. "Who was she?"

"Her name is Marie Zakrzewska, and she is going to become a doctor."

Kitty wrinkled her nose, which has developed enchanting freckles. "Her name is *what?*"

"Dr. Zakrzewska," I repeated.

Kitty's mouth moved silently as she attempted the name. Then she smiled her broad Irish smile. "I shall just call her Dr. Zak," she announced, and went off about her business.

So now "Dr. Zak" has entered my life, and I rejoice in the knowledge.

With Kitty to look after and love, a previously empty part of me seems to have found fulfillment, giving me more energy to devote to such things as my clinic. With the extremely capable assistance of "Dr. Zak," the dispensary is providing medical attention for such a growing number of patients that I think we may soon have to move from our one small room to a larger space.

"Dr. Zak," or Marie, as I call her, is becoming as close a friend as Florence Nightingale was in England. I have remained in correspondence with Florence, and it has been no surprise to me to learn of her success in nursing. She has an indomitable spirit, and an ability to coerce others to her way of thinking. One person she was unable to coerce, however, was Emily.

With the outbreak of the war in the Crimea, Florence found the perfect outlet for her energies. She gathered a group of close to forty female nurses, and with the donation of funds for provisions and supplies, and a somewhat reluctant blessing from England, she headed for Scutari. Before leaving she tried to interest Emily in accompanying her, saying that it might give publicity and impetus to Emily's career. Emily made her own decision—not to go—and wrote me about it. In my reply to her I said:

"I cannot but feel glad that you rejected the urgent persuasions to go to the Crimea. I cannot say what going to Russia might have done for you in *English* reputation, but for America it would have been a sheer waste of time. I am constantly surprised to see what an entire non-conductor of enthusiasm the ocean is, and reputation in England, except in very rare cases, is utterly unavailing here."

As who should know better than I?

Yet I feel certain that Florence will make her name

known, and I shall follow her course with deep interest.

This year of 1854 has brought a small but gratifying increase in my private practice. My accounts tell me that I made fifty dollars more this year than last! Marie has moved quickly and brilliantly through Western Reserve University; the dispensary has expanded into larger quarters on Third Street; and all my interests and efforts are aimed toward establishing a hospital to care for the indigent sick, to train nurses, and to offer women physicians postgraduate hospital experience. A charter has been obtained for such an institution (with eternal blessings on my devoted Quakers) and circulars explaining its purpose have gone out in an effort to raise the needed funds.

Widely respected men have accepted positions as trustees, and are working constantly on my behalf. Men like Horace Greeley, Cyrus W. Field, Charles Butler, Charles A. Dana and Theodore Sedgwick believe in the value of such a hospital, and have succeeded in enlisting an impressive roster of doctors to serve as consultants. As much as it vexes me to acknowledge it, it is obvious that to create the learning-training-treating institution I have in mind I must depend on men to make it a reality. No group of women could accomplish it alone.

Since funds are the first requisite, all manner of means are being resorted to. While the men compose their circulars, stressing (with my very reluctant consent) the training of nurses as the primary purpose, the women are embarked upon a series of fairs, bazaars, and sales. Needles fly, and a seemingly endless stream of scarves and mittens, caps and baby bootees, handkerchiefs and napkins, infant dresses and tray cloths comes pouring out. Some aspects of my "cause" are beyond the scope of these good women to understand, but the employment of their hands to benefit others is natural to them.

I look forward now to Marie's graduation from Western Reserve, and to Emily's return from her study in Europe, so that the three of us can make this dream of mine come true. How much longer will it be?

14 ~ The Hospital

It is ironic that raising money for the hospital required me to close the dispensary for lack of funds. This has been a sad disappointment to me, for I cannot help feeling that I have let these poor people down. Yet it would have been impossible to finance two separate sources of medical aid, and I realize that the hospital will be of more service to more people when and if it becomes a reality. For often my confidence is shaken and my hopes grow slight.

Those dedicated men and women who are devoting themselves to translating my dream into fact have received a host of objections. They have been told that we shall never find a house or building to rent for this purpose, since female physicians would be looked upon with so much suspicion that the police would interfere; that if deaths should occur among the patients the death certificates issued by women doctors would not be recognized; that the only patients willing to enter such an establishment would be of a class or type with which no self-respecting women would deal; that unless men are there as resident physicians it would be impossible to control such patients; that if any accident should take place not only the medical profession would be blamed by the public, but also those hard-working trustees and supporters; and, finally, that in any event it will be impossible to collect sufficient funds for such an unpopular effort.

And still my small "band of believers" continues its work, and it is impossible for me to let them see my own doubts. How odd it is that I, a small, quiet, thirty-five-year-old woman, should be the cause of so much agitation and dissension, and all because I *am* a woman! It is stated that "all men are created equal," but women, most certainly, are not!

"Dr. Zak" is now most truly a doctor with a degree to prove it. She has returned from school, and descended on me like a welcome cloud of energy, establishing herself in practice in the Fifteenth Street house, and listening carefully to all I have to report about our efforts for the hospital. I was telling her about the succession of bazaars when she interrupted.

"They *knit,* these women?" she asked incredulously.

"Oh yes, Marie. Beautiful things! Little caps, and soft shawls, and baby bootees—"

"Elizabeth! Your hospital will never be built on baby bootees!"

"But they want to help. What else can they do?"

"Let them help. Let them knit all the bootees they wish, but we must look much farther than that."

And somehow Marie has found the time and the energy to look farther. She has visited groups of people dedicated to other causes, such as the abolition of slavery, to learn how they go about their fund-raising. She even invaded the bazaar of an antislavery group, was promised a table, stocked it with the despised baby bootees and brought home $650. She has wheedled or browbeaten editors of leading newspapers into publishing articles on our behalf. She has spoken publicly wherever she had the opportunity, requesting donations after each speech. She has renewed my courage so that I, too, have lectured and made appeals for funds.

From England, where she is now completing her studies, an enthusiastic Emily has sent a sizable amount contributed by sympathetic friends.

All this has taken time, which Marie and I have used to search out a suitable building, and we have finally found one. It is an old Dutch house on Bleecker Street, which has been occupied by a family named Roosevelt since early in the century. The present owner, a Mrs. Harriet Roosevelt, has agreed that we may have it, and it only remains now to raise the money. I tremble when I think of how much will be needed to secure the house, and to furnish and heat it. But Marie never seems to doubt, and manages to make me believe all this will really come to pass.

Emily has returned from England, she and Marie have become devoted friends, and we are now a triumvirate to whom things are happening so quickly I have no time nor reason for continued doubt.

We have taken over the Bleecker Street house, and Emily has assumed the great responsibility of converting it into a hospital. She has modeled it on the Children's Hospital in London, and is in firm control. How astonishing to see one's little sister, now an accomplished and superlatively trained surgeon, take command of such a project!

"On no account must we go into debt," says Emily, and limits the number of beds we shall have.

"We will throw the front and back parlors together to make wards," says Emily, and it is done.

"There will be two wards on the second floor with six beds each," says Emily, and the two wards appear.

"The third floor will be the maternity department, the attic will have rooms for students and servants—" Emily says, and I interrupt.

"What servants? How can we afford servants?"

"For students and servants," Emily repeats, and I say no more.

"This large hall will be our sitting room, and in the hall bedroom we will install a great stretch of glass

with many small panes to light it as an operating room.
There will be ample heat from open grate fires."

And I sit in awe and watch it happen.

Quaker friends have brought an abundance of linen
and an unbelievable assortment of furniture. We have
brocaded settees next to cheap wooden chairs, and
beautiful antique pieces ranged beside white utilitar-
ian stands. A variety of curtains and a great number
of plants add to the unusual effect.

While all this has been going on Marie has taken
up residence in the place to keep an eye on the
progress of the work, and Emily and I remain in the
Fifteenth Street house with Kitty. And Emily loves
her just as I knew she would.

In a moment of what I know to be sentimentality, I
chose Florence Nightingale's birthday, May 12, for the
official opening of the New York Infirmary for Women
and Children. It seemed incredible! There we stood,
Emily, Marie, and I, while a great many women and
a very few men walked from floor to floor, peering
into each room. Kitty took delight in following them
about quietly, listening to remarks which she then
came running back to whisper to me. It seemed that
for the most part the reaction was one of surprised
pleasure.

Inevitably I had to speak. I am not quite sure what
I said, but I believe I ended by telling those loyal
people that "The full, thorough education of women
in medicine is a new idea, and, like all other truths,

requires time to prove its value. Women must show
to medical men, even more than to the public, their
capacity to act as physicians, their earnestness as students of medicine, before the existing institutions, with
the great advantages of practice and complete organization, will be opened to them. They must prove
their medical ability before expecting professional
recognition."

If my tongue was in my cheek with that last statement, I trust it was not known. How many years I have
been trying to prove my medical ability, which even
now is regarded with skepticism by the majority.

Dr. Henry Ward Beecher spoke in a thundering
voice that seemed to shake the walls, announcing
flatly that "Woman should be entirely a better physician than man. Her intuition, perception and good
mother wit should make her so." He also roared that
"If the profession of medicine is indelicate for women,
then it is twice as much so for men!"

There were representatives from Horace Greeley's
Tribune and from the *New York Times,* and I was
pleased to see in the next day's papers that the opening was described without the facetious touch which
has long been employed in matters involving "female
tomfoolery."

It has been agreed that Emily will be the surgeon,
Marie the resident physician, and I the director. I
know quite well within myself that both Emily and
Marie are far better doctors than I, and the profession
is more to their taste. I will be much happier in an

administrative position, with just enough practice to keep my hand in.

So now the dream has come to pass, and we must see if we can survive.

15 ⟡ The Hard Years

⟡ Almost immediately the patients from the Tompkins Street dispensary, who seem to me now like old friends, began to come to Bleecker Street, and within a month every bed was occupied. Many of them are foreigners, and they are so grateful because, among the three "doctresses," most European languages are spoken. In the first seven months of the Infirmary's life we cared for 645 medical patients, 227 gynecological, 36 surgical and 18 obstetrical. Patients may pay four dollars a week or nothing, depending on their means, and since few of them have any means it is already becoming clear to me that I shall have to continue pursuing funds.

The famous Fanny Kemble, the Shakespearian actress whom I met when in London, was giving theatrical readings, and when I learned that she often donated the proceeds to worthy institutions, Marie and I went to see her. We arrived at her hotel, and she could not possibly have been more charming as we talked, until the fact that the Infirmary was run entirely by women caught her whole attention. We were then treated to a private performance as she rose to her feet, towering over me, and with flashing eyes and heaving bosom, announced dramatically, "Trust a woman as a doctor—never!"

Which effectively ended that.

In addition to the constant concern for money to run the Infirmary, and the constant pressures of negative public opinion, there have been some frightening times, too.

A large livery stable situated in the rear of the hospital caught fire one afternoon. As sheets of flame became visible through our windows, and the sound of forty stampeding horses filled the wards, our patients succumbed to utter panic.

Marie and Emily and I were hard pressed to soothe them. We sent volunteers to form a bucket line to the roof of the hospital, where they quenched sparks and embers that blew toward us, while we planned how we could move some of the women to a safer area. Before this action was required a God-given wind blew the flames in the opposite direction and the fire was soon extinguished. It was a wearisome day!

Another occasion I wish I could forget was when one of our obstetrical patients died of that dreaded scourge, puerperal fever. Even though we use the utmost care about sanitation and cleanliness during childbirth, including the washing of our hands in a chloride solution advocated by the German, Dr. Semmelweis, this fever still strikes some patients.

I had known how very ill this woman was; I had

even arranged for a close relative to be at her bedside. The relative had sat there, off and on, for the past thirty hours, watching the patient sink farther and farther from life, but when the last fluttering breath was drawn the relative became quite hysterical and accused us of murder. I tried to calm her, and finally sent her home, only to have her return a few hours later with a large ruffianly crowd of other relations and friends, who approached the building waving clubs and pickaxes, and threatening revenge.

We locked and bolted the door, but it would not have withstood for long their beating on it, as they shouted that "the doctresses were killing women in childbirth." It was impossible for any of us to get out of the house to find help, for the mob surrounded the building, and as I heard them pounding on our door I shook with the certainty of what would happen when it gave way. But again we were spared, this time by a great tall Irishman. Members of his family had been treated at the Infirmary and they had nothing but good to say of the place. This giant came crashing through the crowd, waving a shovel over his head, and shouting for attention. Somehow he made himself heard.

"Ye're crazy, the lot o' ye!" he roared. "Who addled you into a mess like this? Those three doctors in there are good women who do the best they can for thankless whelps like you, and most of ye know that! Now, clear off! Get on your way and leave the doctors in peace to tend your sick!"

And somehow, with the aid of a watchman who arrived belatedly, this great wonderful man succeeded in scattering the crowd and leaving us in safety.

That was not the only time we were accused of killing our patients. Another woman died of a ruptured appendix, and the following day a crowd gathered and stood outside, shouting that the Infirmary was run by "women cranks who kill their patients with cold water!" This time Emily managed to get a message to Dr. Kissam, who was our consultant from Bellevue Hospital. While we waited, praying he would come, the angry mob outside threw stones at our windows, sending our patients into spasms of fear as the glass shattered and fell to the floor.

Dr. Kissam came promptly. We could see his horse galloping down the street, lathered and straining, and the doctor standing up in his swaying carriage, shouting as he came. He plunged the conveyance into the crowd, effectually dividing them, pulled up at the door, and then jumped out and mounted the steps. From there he spoke calmly.

"About fifteen of you come inside," he ordered. "The closest members of the family—that's all! And drop those insane weapons at the door!"

He stood back and allowed a number of the people, almost all men, to enter the Infirmary. They seemed suddenly subdued, like guilty children, but their faces were still cold and angry.

"Now listen to me closely," Dr. Kissam said. "I was consulted on this case, and I advised cold compresses, which is the customary and standard treatment. But nothing in God's world could have saved that woman! Her appendix ruptured, spewing poison into the rest of her system."

One of the men glowered at him. "That's what you say," he growled. "How do we know it's true?"

Dr. Kissam stared at him a moment, and then made up his mind. "I will prove it to you," he said. "The coroner is on his way, at my request. We will perform an autopsy, and you are invited to watch, and draw your own conclusions. Will that satisfy you?"

If it had not been so alarming, it would have been comical! The men and women looked at each other, and their distaste for the suggestion was plain on their faces, yet pride would not allow them to refuse. At last twelve of the men gathered with the coroner, Dr. Kissam, Emily, and myself, and the autopsy proceeded. The findings were carefully explained as they were revealed, and except for one poor soul who retched and then fainted, the affair was concluded. The weak member, now revived and looking rather green, joined the other eleven in declaring themselves convinced that nothing could have prevented the woman's death.

As they left the hospital, with as much speed as they could manage, they looked at me apologetically, and I could see they wanted to speak but could find no words. I opened the door for them and stood beside it, and I smiled.

"You could not help your feelings," I told them.

"We women doctors, after all, have to prove ourselves."

They straggled out, I closed the door and leaned against it. I could feel myself shaking.

We continue to try to prove ourselves, but often with most unlikely instruments. When we started our training course for nurses we offered free teaching of four months' duration, and then hopefully awaited the intelligent, educated women we wanted as recruits. Instead we were approached by some of the most unsavory characters it has been my misfortune to see. Dirty, often beer-soaked, failures at other work—what a collection they were! Some few were extremely voluble eccentrics who followed the trend toward short hair and Mrs. Amelia Bloomer's trousers, arousing instant antagonism among the patients. There were, of course, a very few candidates of the sort we were looking for, and we added the best of the rest, some of whom surprised us by coming much closer to our ideals during the nursing course.

But the work and worry are constant. I find myself submerged in the problems of raising money, soothing patients, calming their relatives, maintaining good relations with our trustees, overseeing the running of the hospital, keeping a loving eye on Kitty—the days are never long enough, and at times I ache with fatigue.

Still, I can see that we are becoming stronger in every way. The number of patients increases steadily, more and more people are losing their mistrust of female physicians, and gradually we are enlisting support. The road has been a long and hard one, but I think it has been worthwhile. In any event, I could not have done differently.

16 ✆ *Paris*

✆ One of the joys of being part of a large family is visiting back and forth. Since it is difficult for us to leave the hospital for any length of time, Emily's and my brothers, sisters and mother come and go from the Fifteenth Street house, staying a few hours, a few days or a few weeks. None of the Blackwells remains in one place very long; we all like moving about. We no longer rent any part of the house since finances are not as stringent as they once were, though I am sure I shall never have to worry about my personal fortune!

My brother Samuel married a charming young woman named Antoinette Brown—a preacher, if you please!—and they came to stay with me when their first baby was due, so that I had the deep pleasure of delivering my niece, Florence. Kitty was delighted at having "a live doll" in the house, and spent hours holding the infant and crooning to her. My brother Henry is also married, to a pretty young woman named Lucy Stone, who insists upon using her maiden name, and is becoming recognized as a gifted lecturer on women's rights.

Sister Marian spends most of her time at the Fifteenth Street house, though on occasion she goes back to Ohio to see Mother, or bravely crosses the ocean to visit Anna, who seems to have made Paris her permanent home. George and Howard and Ellen drift in and out whenever they are in New York, and Mother pays state visits from time to time. All of these dear people make much of Kitty, who tells me constantly that she never knew how nice it was to have a large family.

"At first I didn't have anybody," she said recently, "and then I had you, and all of a sudden I had a whole crowd of aunts and uncles and cousins! It makes me feel like a real *person!*"

And it makes me feel quite at ease when I have to leave Kitty as much as I do. Her hours after school are not lonely, since there seems always to be some Blackwell to keep an eye on her. Not that Kitty needs watching. She is becoming so capable and dependable that I have even entrusted her with paying some of the household bills. I think she most enjoys paying our baker, for whenever she enters Simpson's with the money, she exits with a fresh warm bun or the end slice of a new loaf. I teased her about it once, and she said, "I should like to be all made of Simpson's bread! It's better than anything!"

All during this hard time, when the Infirmary has been struggling with its beginnings, I have kept in touch with all the friends I made in England. More and more their letters are starting to contain a single request.

"Won't you please come back to England, if only for a visit? We need you. There are so many women here who are interested in medicine, but no progress is being made in accepting them. There is much you could do! We will arrange lectures for you, raise money for you—please come!"

I have considered this seriously, knowing I could be of service there, both by arousing interest in the concept of women in medicine, and by raising funds to help with the Infirmary here, but it has seemed as though I would be deserting a responsibility of my own making were I to leave the hospital now. I discussed it at length with Emily and Marie not long ago, and they both urged me to accept the invitation.

"Marie and I can certainly take care of things here," Emily said. "At last we have some excellent nurses; our trustees and supporters are constantly advancing our cause, and money is not quite the desperate problem it was."

"All those baby bootees!" Marie sighed. "They are still being made!"

"And sold," Emily pointed out. "Those fairs are important to us. I think you should go, Elizabeth. If you have any faith in us at all, believe that we can manage."

So—I think I shall.

I decided to take Kitty with me, which threw her into ecstasy, and in August of 1858 we sailed on the Cunard ship, the *Persia*. As usual I spent most of the time being deathly seasick in the cabin, but Kitty enjoyed herself thoroughly, and made friends with everyone on board.

At Liverpool we were met by Brother Howard, looking very brown and fit after some time in India. (Have I not said that the Blackwells travel about a great deal?) He went with us to London where we stayed for a few days with Ellen, who has been studying art in France and England. Kitty seemed to absorb London through her pores, loving every varying facet of it, just as I always have. She was not overly pleased when I told her I thought an English boarding school would be a good idea.

"But I'd rather go with you, Doctor! Why can't I go with you?"

"I don't really know where I'll be going, Kitty. And you can't just stop your schooling."

"I would study all the time we went places. Truly I would!"

"No, darling. School for a while at least, really."

And yet when I left her at the excellent boarding school in Surrey, I could not forget her sad, wistful little face gazing after me. I had given her several stamped, addressed envelopes in which to send me letters, but they seemed cold comfort to a little girl temporarily abandoned in a strange country.

I went on to Paris to visit Anna, who seems to have made quite a name for herself as a writer and news correspondent. No less a writer than Edgar Allan Poe has called her "a real woman of letters." Anna took me to a reception at Compiegne where the beautiful Empress Eugénie appeared in a cherry velvet dress covered with lace. I was captivated by her hair style and promptly wrote Kitty about it.

"The Empress's hair was cut very short in the front," I told her, "and curled in tiny ringlets across her forehead. I have studied it closely, and I may perhaps try it on you. Or should I start with Dr. Emily?"

I knew that would make Kitty smile, for Emily cares very little about her appearance as long as she is neat and clean, and she pulls her hair back as tight as it will go lest it drift in her face during an operation.

But it was going to take more than a letter from me to make Kitty enjoy the English school. Poor darling! There was no mail from her for quite a while, and I relaxed with the happy thought that all was well, when at last a letter came. It was neatly written except for small blots of ink from what I gathered was a very excited pen.

DEAR DOCTOR: I do *not* like it here! I wrote you another letter about the dreadful treacle pudding, that everyone likes but me because it has crusts as thick as boards and it bounces out of my dish, and I wrote you about if you're even a little late for breakfast or prayers they send you to bed for the *whole day,* and I wrote you about having to curtsey all the time and I don't do it very well, and I wrote you about everybody being surprised that I could speak English and I got cross and said What should I speak? and then they said I was impudent, but Somebody reads all the students' letters and when they read mine to you they didn't send it and I don't want to stay! I am going to carry this letter with me until we go on a walk and I find a place to mail it myself.

All my love,
KITTY

I wept, and then brushed the tears away quickly and wrote that Kitty was to leave school and go to stay with Ellen in London. I knew she would be safe and happy there for a short while until I could get her to Paris. Kitty told me later that when she was told she was leaving school it was the next-to-happiest day of her short life.

"What was the happiest?" I asked.

"When you adopted me, of course."

I then arranged for Howard, still in London, to put Kitty on the boat for Dieppe, feeling he would be better able to cope with passports than Ellen, in which I was correct. A passport had never been issued to a child, and it took all Howy's efforts to manage it. The next move was a letter to a friend in Dieppe, asking her to meet the boat and see that Kitty got on the right train for Paris.

And having accomplished all this, I arrived at the wrong station to meet her! There was no sign of her when I got out of my cab at the station, and a few questions convinced me of my mistake. I set off as quickly as I could for the Chemin de Fer de l'Ouest, and there again I searched everywhere, looking for some trace of a small redhaired girl, feeling more and more frightened when I could not spy her anywhere. At last I spoke to a group of station officials and was greeted with long streams of rapid French.

Mais certainement, they had seen *la petite!* Her trunk had been examined, and everyone had waited to see who would meet this small girl traveling alone. When no one appeared they had questioned her, asking where she wanted to go. Kitty produced Anna's address on a scrap of paper, and asked for a fiacre to take her there. Dubiously the men had complied, had fastened her trunk on top, and watched with misgivings as she was driven away.

Thanking them, I found myself another hansom cab and started back to Anna's, staring at every vehicle on the street. I don't believe I have ever felt such relief as in the moment I saw her little trunk tied on top of another fiacre! I called to my driver to stop and leaned out of the window.

"Is that you, child?" I called.

A small frightened face, blue eyes wide, looked out at me.

"Doctor!" she cried.

Another moment and I was in the cab beside her, her head tight against my shoulder. I think perhaps I never knew before how much I love my Kitty!

17 ✤ London and Home Again

✤This year abroad with Kitty has been a busy one. I did not urge school on her for a few weeks, and we enjoyed ourselves with long walks around Paris, and giving Kitty an opportunity to practice her French. After a bit, however, I found a boarding school for American children which seemed agreeable to Kitty. Once installed she was totally satisfied, and I found my days filled to overflowing.

I revisited La Maternité, half hoping, I suppose, to find M. Blot still there, but when he was not, I did not ask where he might be. Medicine has taught me there are certain things which can never be revived. I inspected many hospitals around the city, had long and illuminating talks with the leading physicians, and prepared lectures to be given in England. After Christmas, which Kitty shared with Anna and me, I deposited her safely back in school, and went to England.

I had received a letter from Florence Nightingale, asking me to come and see her in Malvern for the purpose of discussing a school she hoped to found for the training of nurses, and I was in high spirits when I arrived there. What a shock! I had expected to see the tall, vigorous woman I had left some years ago, but instead I found a hollow-eyed, fragile, exhausted friend, but one whose indomitable spirit seemed still to blaze. Her terrible, wonderful years in the Crimea had sapped her bodily strength, but the essence of her —all that made her so dear to me—had become a flame of energy. Her voice was still vibrant as she talked of the incredible feats she had accomplished.

It was Florence who revolutionized the British army's health program, engineered the Royal Sanitary Commission, and devised the regulations for a school that would provide training in military hygiene and surgery. It was Florence who had published a book entitled *Notes on Hospitals,* which had shocked the English nation with its revelation of filthy rooms, walls, floors and beds, poor and inadequate food for patients, insufficient and unsanitary disposal of all wastes, wretched and unskilled nursing. She proclaimed the high mortality rate as unnecessary and preventable, and went so far as to say that hospitals generally did their patients more harm than good.

Now with this boundless knowledge and experience to draw on, Florence hoped to found a nursing school, and wished me to be its director!

"There is already forty-five thousand pounds," she said, "so we need not skimp ourselves. And there will be more, Elizabeth."

The prospect was tempting, but there were so many things to consider.

"I should want Emily to work with me," I told her. "I cannot simply abandon my sister. And she would want to pursue private practice, I am sure."

"Private practice would have no place in this," Florence said impatiently. "There would be no time for it."

I found myself wondering whether Emily's refusal to join Florence in the Crimea still rankled, but I said nothing.

"In any case," she went on, "leave that to the men, Elizabeth. There are too many important things that women can do better—and *should* be doing!"

I promised to consider the matter, but I think I knew already that it was not the work I should be doing. A great work, but not for me. Nor Emily, either.

The next several months were spent in delivering the lectures I had prepared. These dealt primarily with the opening of the medical profession to women, and their specific need to understand more about hygiene, and how the lack of it causes or intensifies some of the unutterable diseases that afflict females. A great deal of interest has been raised, and will, I trust, continue. I have had many offers—to open a medical school, to head a sanitarium, to build a hospital for women—none of which I feel I can accept while my own New York Infirmary is still in need of guidance. England is dear to me, and I always feel it is my home and in time I should like to settle here. But the time is not yet.

One triumph, however, I cherish, and have accepted with pride. On January 1 of this year, 1859, the Medical Register of the United Kingdom entered on its rolls for the first time the name of a woman physician, Dr. Elizabeth Blackwell!

In August Kitty and I returned to New York to find several changes. Marie, after fulfilling her promise of two years' unpaid service to the Infirmary, had left to superintend a department in a Boston hospital. This was an excellent opportunity for her, though she writes that she is not satisfied with the standards in obstetrics.

"I am thinking of founding a hospital for women and children that will be built on my own beliefs (and the thousand things I have learned from you)," she wrote, "but in the meantime my private practice flourishes and I continue at this hospital, saving money, making friends and taking notes."

I smiled. Apparently Marie was not thinking in terms of baby bootees. I mentioned this to her when I answered her letter, and went on to say:

"I work chiefly in principles, and you in putting them into practical use; and one is essential to the other in this complex life of ours. You are a natural doctor, and your best work will always be in the full exercise of direct medical work. You know I am different from you in not being a natural doctor; so, naturally, I do not confine myself to practice. I am never without some patients, but my thought, and active interest, is chiefly given to some of those moral ends, for which I took up the study of medicine."

Emily had had the full responsibility of running the Infirmary, and had achieved a great deal. Several female graduates from Philadelphia medical schools had come to us for their practical hospital experience, and had proved themselves in every way. We were training more and better nurses, and expanding the services which the Infirmary provided. I was concerned with the realization that the lease on Bleecker Street was about to expire, but a permanent fund, which had been started some years ago, for the purchase of a new site, had now grown to gratifying proportions. With our solid backing of clear-eyed Quakers, we promptly purchased a large house on Second Avenue and began adapting it to hospital purposes.

It was Emily's idea to sell the Fifteenth Street house.

"There is plenty of living space in the new building," she pointed out, "and it will save the cost of maintaining two establishments. Besides, it will make it easier for both of us if we live right here on the premises."

So in our laying out of the rooms in the Second Avenue building, we included small apartments for Emily and Marian, and for Kitty and me. There was much to be done, and Emily went about the business with great efficiency. We planned the actual moving day carefully so that there would be a minimum of patients to transport, but we still made quite an impressive sight as we officially moved into our new home.

Taking advantage of the additional space and the

new equipment, we have enlarged the services which the Infirmary offers, and established a new post, that of Sanitary Visitor. Intelligent young Dr. Rebecca Cole, a graduate of the Woman's Medical College of Pennsylvania, and the first Negro woman physician, is heading this work. Dr. Cole's workers visit dispensary cases, distribute pamphlets carrying elementary rules for health and cleanliness, report unsanitary conditions, and try to educate poor mothers in the proper care of infants and fundamental health rules. The workers carry in their bags such items as sponges, scrubbing brushes, soap, and disinfectant, and their enthusiastic wielding of these weapons already shows an improvement in conditions.

I have also started thinking of a medical college for women, to work in conjunction with the Infirmary. On Bleecker Street we were able to supply hospital experience for young female doctors, but I should like to supervise the entire medical training, with the very best in teaching staff and equipment. It seems to be the next logical step in my self-imposed program of helping women establish themselves in medicine, and having gone this far, I cannot stop now.

18 ∾ *The War Years*

∾How bravely I said that! "I cannot stop now." Many hopes and dreams stopped for all America on April 12, 1861, when the first shot in a civil war was fired at Fort Sumter. Since childhood I have been raised in the belief that slavery is wrong, and that all men are created equal. That belief is now the essence of a struggle that threatens to tear the country apart. It is also, quite evidently, going to tax every hospital and every person with medical training, no matter to what degree.

Emily and I called all the managers and trustees of the New York Infirmary for Women and Children together to discuss the need for nurses. Somehow the meeting was mentioned in the *New York Times* and our building was so overcrowded with people wanting to help that there were long lines in the street waiting for entrance. There seemed to be a perfect mania among the women to act Florence Nightingale!

This indicated that perhaps we should link ourselves with the national plan of action, and as a result we called for a public meeting to be held at Cooper Union. From this second meeting two organizations have been born: the United States Sanitary Aid Commission and the Women's Central Relief Association. The latter is designed to receive and distribute various comforts for the soldiers, and to this end scores of women work daily at Cooper Union. But the specific function is to supply nurses, and I have found myself working as head of the Registration Committee.

Women flock to be trained as nurses—women of every level of intelligence, physical strength, and moral quality. With only a few moments to spare for each one, I have had to decide immediately which were the most promising candidates, and arrange for a month's training—so pitifully inadequate!—at the New York Hospital, Bellevue, or our own Infirmary. They are then outfitted and sent on to Washington, where a knowledgeable woman named Dorothea Dix has been made Superintendent of Nurses.

It has not been easy. In addition to my private practice and the work at the Infirmary, I now have to cope with the blunders and muddling of a govern-ment that was ill prepared for war. There has been a strong feeling that women are merely calling attention to themselves—more of their Women's Rights antics, no doubt—and that in all probability they would only be "in the way" if they ever got near actual battle conditions. I hope some of the men who said such things eat their words!

For example, there is a German woman, one of the many I interviewed, who was accepted, trained, and sent to Washington. Somehow she managed to elude Miss Dix's corps of nurses, and made her way to Gettysburg where a battle was coming to a climactic finish. For two sleepless days and nights she trudged the battlefield in a pair of soldier's boots. Through the blood and the mud she pulled living men from beneath dead ones, bandaged their wounds, gave them water, and in short did everything within her nursing and feminine ability to save lives and ease pain. "In the way?" I hardly think so.

The hospital has continued to prosper during these war years, which have lasted longer, I think, than anyone ever envisioned. Although Emily and I have frequently worked around the clock with our seemingly endless obligations, our finances, at least, are no longer a major worry.

For several years I have wanted a home out of the city where Kitty and I could occasionally get away from the hospital and its constant demands, and now, aided by the sale of the Fifteenth Street house, I felt I could invest in such a property. My brother Henry and his clever, pretty wife, Lucy Stone, have bought a comfortable rambling farmhouse in West Bloomfield, New Jersey, and they invited Kitty and me there several times. It is a lovely spot, quiet and peaceful, and with a view in the distance of New York Bay. I sat there sometimes, talking with Lucy, and thinking it would be a restful place to spend my scant free time. Lucy was enthusiastic.

"Oh, do, Elizabeth! If you had a place near us here, just think of all the good talks we could have!"

I smiled at my dark-eyed sister-in-law. "I should think you would be filled with talk, Lucy. All those lectures!"

"I know. Women's rights!" She gave a mock sigh, and then giggled. "There are those who say it may be a woman's right to talk, but that I overdo it."

"They are just envious of how much you accomplish. Lucy, if it weren't for you—well! Women must learn to stand on their own two feet! To depend on their own abilities instead of always on a man!"

Lucy laughed softly. "And yet there was a time, after little Alice was born, when I felt I had no right to tell any woman what to do. I was so in love with Henry—I still am!—and so dependent on his love for me. How could I tell other women to be independent?"

"Perhaps daring to love is a form of independence," I said. "It brings with it responsibilities that cannot be taken lightly."

"You sound like Henry. It was he who urged me to start lecturing again, and I am glad he did. I have even more to tell women now, because I know what it is to be completely fulfilled. I have a husband and a daughter to love—and how much I love them!— and I have a career, if one can call it that, on which to spend my energies. I truly have a woman's rights, and sometimes it makes me feel very humble." She stopped and looked at me, her eyes serious. "You make me feel humble, too, Elizabeth. You have done so much more by example than I can ever hope to accomplish by lecturing. But—" Lucy laid a small hand on my arm. "May I ask you something?"

"Of course."

"Have you ever been in love, Elizabeth?"

Unconsciously I raised my hand and laid it across that wretched glass eye, and my mind was suddenly filled with a name it has not touched in years. Hippolyte Blot. It was a moment before I could speak.

"I think I never loved as you do, sister, or perhaps

I never had your courage. I had to become the first woman doctor. It was a goal that left little room for anything else."

"And now you have reached that goal. Is it enough?"

"I have Kitty, too," I said. "Together—yes, together it is enough."

But sometimes I can't help wondering.

In any event, I was so taken with Henry's and Lucy's house that I have built a cottage of my own quite near them. I had a dual purpose in mind. At the moment it does admirably for Kitty and me when we can get away from New York, but also I have thoughts of possibly enlarging it someday into a convalescent home. In the meantime we spend Sundays there, and sometimes whole weekends, delighting in the quiet, the freshness of the air, and the soft undulating countryside.

We were there, Kitty and I, one summer day in 1863 when word flew from neighbor to neighbor that riots had broken out in New York. The tinder was certainly there! There were many southern sympathizers in the city, as well as abolitionists and Negroes, and fighting had been frequent. Added to that was the Draft Law, which proclaimed that all men between 20 and 45 were liable for the draft, but that a man could be excused if he could supply a substitute, or could buy his way out for $300. For those who could do neither it was additional provocation. The weather was dismally hot and humid, tempers were high—and the match was struck. When I heard that a mob was forming, composed mostly of foreign-born laboring men who intended to break into the Second Avenue arsenal for guns and ammunition, I knew I had to go to the Infirmary.

"You must stay here, Kitty. You will be all right. I shall be back as soon as I can."

Kitty's voice was sharp with emotion. "Don't be ridiculous! You know perfectly well I am not going to let you go alone, Doctor!"

There seemed no point in argument. As we crossed the river on a ferry in the summer dusk, we could see the low skyline brightened by flames. At the dock the streets seemed so empty I thought we should never find a hansom, but at last one came careening along to unload a group of people, obviously on their way out of the city. It took all my persuasive powers and some extra cash to hire the cab for the trip to the hospital, but I managed it, and we departed with such speed Kitty and I clutched each other and the leather straps lest we be thrown out.

We passed groups of men forming into larger crowds, carrying clubs and pitchforks, old guns or shovels, any weapon they had been able to lay their hands on. By the light of their torches their faces were uncontrolled and threatening, and I found myself praying that Kitty and I would reach the Infirmary unharmed.

We did, and Emily let us in quickly and bolted the door.

"You shouldn't have come," she said, "but thank

God you did! Oh, Elizabeth, I am really afraid!"

"So am I," I said grimly, "but we can't stand here quaking. How are the patients?"

"Frantic! The white ones want us to send the black ones out of here. They are positive we'll be burned to the ground because there are Negroes in the building."

"We're not sending anyone out of here, black or white! Come along, Emily, let's see what we can do to calm things down. Kitty, you can help."

I know something now of what war must be like. None of us slept that night—I doubt that anyone in the city slept. From the windows in the hospital I could see carts loaded with household goods taken from looted homes, drawn by bragging, bellowing, swearing men. Telegraph wires were torn down and streetcar rails pulled up. Negroes ran through the streets for their lives, and many of them lost. They were caught and beaten to death, or hanged from street lamps, and I choked with nausea as I adjusted heavy curtains so that none of the patients could glimpse the madness outside.

In the morning the heat was heavy, but I dared not open any windows. During the day flames licked hungrily all over the city, and when ten or eleven houses a block north of us were set afire, there was no way I could prevent the glare from reaching our terrified patients. Emily and Kitty and I, and anyone else on the staff with enough control to manage it, walked in and out of the wards all that day, soothing, calming, covering the patients' faces with sheets to shut out the dancing flame light. We adhered to the hospital schedule as closely as we could in an effort to create some sense of security, but all of us knew what an empty gesture it was.

Our black women patients, many of whom had escaped from the south, moaned and shuddered, and who could blame them? Late in the afternoon a thunderstorm broke, shaking our whole building with its ferocity, but helping to quell the flames outside.

There would have been no object in asking for police to protect the Infirmary; the mob had over-powered almost all police and militia. Once or twice someone we knew would bang on the door and be ad-mitted to tell of the latest horrors. A colored children's orphanage had been set afire, but by some providence of God the two hundred children had been led to safety by a back door. What would happen to them, homeless and hunted, I dared not think.

This incredible hysteria lasted for four days. Shops were closed and boarded up in a vain effort to save them from looters, so we had no way of getting pro-visions. Meals became a problem, but no one had much appetite for food. A few relatives of the patients made their way to us by night, and some, especially the Negroes, pleaded with us to let them stay.

A frightened little nurse gathered her courage and spoke to me.

"Do you realize what may happen to us if that mob should break in here and find those black people?" she whispered.

I glared at her out of my one good eye. "And do you realize what may happen to those black people if we send them out of here? You are too young to have that on your conscience. Now, go back to work and try to keep your hands from shaking. You might drop one of the babies."

For a moment I thought she was going to argue, but then she managed a tremulous smile. "Yes, Dr. Black-well," she said. "You needn't worry, ma'am. I'll be all right. Thank you."

And turning, she tried to walk down the corridor in a crisp, professional manner, but I noticed with sympathy that she scuttled past the windows, averting her eyes from the constant glare outside.

Babies were born, Emily performed several operations, medicines were given, and the usual hospital care went on, all against that mad background of carnage that lay outside our windows.

On the fourth day New York's famous 7th Regiment was rushed back from the Gettysburg campaign, and, aided by the strengthened militia and police, with help from naval forces and West Point cadets, the rioting was brought to a halt. I am told that more than a thousand people died, and the damage by fire, breakage, and looting runs into an astronomical figure.

But somehow the Infirmary was untouched. If ever I prayed my thanks to God, it was then.

And the war goes on. More and more houses show the black crepe of mourning on their doors, and there are fewer and fewer men on the streets. The papers bring us news of battles won and lost, carrying long columns of the names of the dead. Stories of the heroism of many of our nurses are brought back to us, too, and occasionally some of them, sent home for a brief respite, come to see us at the Infirmary. They are thinner, and their eyes seem shadowed by the misery they have seen, but there is not one who regrets having committed herself.

"If only we could have had more thorough training," they tell me. "If only there had been more time for it. With so few doctors, there would have been much more we could have done for the wounded—if we had been taught how."

More and better training. In *everything!* That is what women must have.

The fighting has gone on for four years now. It is hard to believe! We seem to have lived this way forever, always tired, always a little hungry, always shocked when we hear of another death among men we knew, yet somehow contriving to live normal daily lives, even forgetting briefly that a war still rages.

An invitation came to me recently to speak at a meeting of the Sanitation Commission in Washington, and I accepted it mainly because it offered a chance to break this harrowing routine. How glad I am that I went!

Traveling through Maryland, which has just freed its slaves, I was overjoyed to see free black men on the roads. What a pleasure it was! Washington itself was grimmer, since the wounded were constantly being brought in. Often I watched the efforts of men to steady the swaying wagons that carried their injured comrades to hospitals, and these processions were sad indeed. I met Miss Dorothea Dix, a dedicated woman who has been performing a priceless service, but the most stirring hour of my visit was under the guidance of my old friend, Dr. Elder of Philadelphia. He met me in Washington, and escorted me to meet President Lincoln!

A tall, ungainly, loose-jointed man was standing in the middle of the room, and he came forward with a pleasant smile and shook hands with me. I think I never saw an uglier man, nor one who so radiated strength and kindness. Quite informally he sat his long body down on the corner of a table, caught up one knee, looking for all the world like a Kentucky loafer on some old tavern steps, and began to discuss some point about the war. When we left him I could not rid myself of the feeling that I had been in the presence of a great man.

On Palm Sunday, 1865, the news reached us that the war was over. I could not absorb it. General Lee had surrendered to General Grant at Appomattox, and the dreadful specter of slavery was—we were told—a thing of the past.

In the softness of that spring evening Kitty and I went for a walk. The streets were filled with people, all strolling as we were, all trying to fit the conception of peace into their lives. Bands were playing gay songs like "Yankee Doodle," and "Lanigan's Ball" and "We'll All Drink Stone Blind," and Kitty's step took on a happy strut as she walked beside me. Children ran and laughed, caught up in the carnival air, forgetting, perhaps, that many of their fathers or brothers would never walk these streets again.

Kitty was excited, too. Humming softly, half skipping, she could not contain her pleasure. Her bright, pretty, seventeen-year-old face glowed.

"It's all going to be different now, isn't it, Doctor? Everything is going to be different!"

"I hope so, Kitty."

"Just look at people's faces! They are smiling—almost all of them! I don't remember seeing so many people smile before."

"It has been a long time."

"We should do something to celebrate! Something —*exciting!*"

I smiled at her enthusiasm. "Such as what?"

"Oh, I don't know! Something we haven't been able to do all the time the war was going on."

I found myself infected by her gaiety. "Let's have some new clothes made," I said, in true feminine response. "Neither of us has had a really pretty new frock in years. We both need something bright and fresh and just a little giddy!"

"Oh, Doctor! Could we? Could we afford it?"

"Of course! What would you like?"

"Something with plaid on it! I do so love plaid! A very pale material—pearl color, maybe, with plaid trimming! Oh, how lovely! May we, *really?*"

"Really."

· "And what about you, Doctor? What will you have?"

Solemnly I said, "I think I shall have plaid also. Bands of it sewed on my doctorial sack."

Kitty burst into delighted laughter at my small joke. "You will have more than that, I swear you will! I shall see to it that you do!" Then she sobered and looked at me searchingly. "You are tired, aren't you, Doctor? We'll go home now, and you will sleep to-night. Everything is going to be different now. Everything is going to be better."

Slowly we walked home, and that night I slept deeply and dreamlessly, waking with a wonderful feeling of hope and expectancy. I think Kitty is right. Everything is going to be different now. Everything is going to be better.

19 ⁀ The College

⁀There is, indeed, a difference, and it shows itself most clearly among women. There are those who had to assume authority and responsibility when their men were away, and many of these will have to continue without the husbands or fathers on whom they former-ly depended. Others, having tasted an unfamiliar freedom, are not about to give it up. Women have proved themselves in many ways through necessity, desire, or natural instinct, and I think they will not return to their narrow lives.

What is even more important is that a far greater female independence is now accepted with little preju-dice, which means that many doors have been opened that were previously closed. And one of these is medicine.

The years of war have taught the nation the im-portance of medical care and thorough training, both for doctors and for nurses, and with this thought in mind I have talked to the trustees of the Infirmary.

"I think it is time to establish a medical college for women," I said bravely. "The Infirmary seems to be in good favor in the city, and I believe a college charter could be achieved."

"Why involve yourself, Elizabeth? Why assume this additional responsibility when you could urge women to attend already established schools? There is Cornell, for example—"

"There is, indeed! And for seven years Emily and I have been recommending women to Cornell, which *claims* to be coeducational. In every case they have been refused. There is also something else. The majority of the women who *have* been accepted at various schools, and heaven knows they are few, have been of an inferior type. They are opportunists, rather than dedicated medical students. As a result the quality of the education given them is declining. I want to see much better training—and much more of it!"

"But training now seems adequate—"

I sat up very straight. "Training now, in many of the so-called 'good' schools, often lasts no more than ten months. *Ten months!* And generally without one day's practical experience! Lectures and lectures and lectures—but no chance for a student to observe a patient. If he is fortunate enough to make his way into a hospital and watch an operation, it is from such a distance that it is virtually invisible to him! The examinations are inadequate, and the ground left uncovered is enormous. I want more than that, gentlemen. Much more!"

They listened, bless them, and they have acted. A college charter has been granted to the New York Infirmary for Women and Children, and we begin now to plan our program. Again, I am being adamant about many aspects of it.

"I want strict entrance examinations," I have told my trustees, "conducted by a special examining board that will be independent of the teaching staff. I want to make sure that the women we accept are going to be a credit to us as doctors. I want longer terms of study in a course that will take four years."

"Four years, Elizabeth!"

"Four years! With constant clinical experience in the wards of the Infirmary, under the best teaching staff we can find. And I want to establish hygiene as one of the principal studies, both equal and obligatory. When our women graduate, gentlemen, I want them to be *physicians,* not simply to scrawl M.D. after their names."

And I have had my way. The best New York doctors have agreed to teach or to give specific lectures. An examining board is being selected and entrance requirements laid out. The news that such a medical college is about to open has inundated us with requests for admission, and somehow—after the years of struggling and hoping—it all seems too easy. But as Kitty said, everything is going to be different now. Everything is going to be better.

November, 1868, and the College—I use a capital "C" now that it is a reality—is open. I find myself occupying the position of Professor of Hygiene with supreme delight and untold pride! At the opening it was deemed necessary for me to speak, and I did so from my heart.

In part I said, "Medicine is a learned and confidential profession and should draw to its ranks the most highly educated, the most irreproachable in character. This most noble profession, like all high things, is susceptible to the worst abuse. The good which women may accomplish in medical practice is also the measure of the evil they may do. Education, long and careful, should be the safeguard of society in this matter. . . . The College must be an honest and earnest attempt to give women the very highest education that modern science can afford. Let us give all due weight to sympathy," I went on, "and never dispense with it in the true physician; but it is knowledge, not sympathy, which can administer the right medicine. It is observation and comprehension, not sympathy, which will discover the kind of diseases; and though warm sympathetic natures, with knowledge, would make the best of all physicians—without sound knowledge, they would be most unreliable and dangerous guides."

So now the New York |Infirmary| and College are established and operating successfully. I am forty-seven years old, and I do feel in all honesty that those years have been well spent. The social isolation, the hard work, the combatting of prejudice, the loneliness, the many fears and obstacles have finally been surmounted, and the result is here around me, visible and tangible. It is not a bad record for an old-maid woman doctor!

20 ∾ 1869. The Going

∾ I have been sitting here in my little office, thinking over the years, and I have come to a decision. As a result, I have asked Emily to come and talk to me.

I look at her as she enters. She is much taller than I, with a strong, calm face framed in thick reddish hair which shows no sign of gray as mine does. She is only five years younger than I, and yet she seems to have a vigor and an energy that I no longer have in such quantities. She is capable, and vital, and wise, and my decision is suddenly stronger than ever.

"Emily," I say, "I am going to leave the Infirmary for you to run. Actually you have done so for the past several years, while I fussed over the College and spent time on my other interests. Now it is time that you take over completely."

She looks at me serenely. "And you are going back to England."

I can't suppress a small gasp. "How did you know?"

"Because you have wanted to live and work there for many years, Elizabeth. I have known that."

I smile sheepishly. "I didn't realize I had made it so plain. But you are quite right. We are not both needed here now, the real pioneer work of women in medicine is finished in America. We both know of the special schools for women that have been sanctioned in Boston and Philadelphia and here in New York, with better training than ever before."

"Largely based on this one," Emily says warmly.

"I like to think so. But the fact remains that in England the work is still to do. That's where I want to be now, Emily."

"Then go, my dear! Go, and God bless you! Will you take Kitty?"

"Of course. I don't think I could manage very long without Kitty. She *fits* me, Emily."

My sister smiles. "I know. Like an eiderdown quilt,

she tucks into all your corners. Very well, then, let me know what your plans are, dear."

"I will."

Emily rises and starts for the door, but turns back to me.

"And when you get to England, sister, give 'em 'what for!' " She grins at me, her eyes sparkling. "I pity the poor Britons, Elizabeth. They have no idea what's about to happen to them!"

And then she leaves.

As for me, my feelings are mixed. There is much satisfaction in simply staying here and surveying the continued success of our hospital and the College; in seeing more and more women turn to medicine as a profession, and in being able to give them the best training available; in seeing the hospital death rate diminish even as the number of patients increases. But—England! It is the country I love most, and it has always been kind to me. I have far more close friends there than here, and I have heard from all of them continually since my last visit. They are eager for me to come back, and have promised support of every kind in opening a medical future to Englishwomen. And I *want* to go!

It is summer, and tomorrow I sail for England. Tonight I took a last walk through the Infirmary, pacing the corridors, going into each room and speaking to every patient. I thought of the growth of the hospital, starting with my dreary little dispensary in Tompkins Square, through the troubles at Bleecker Street, and on to the present building with the dreadful war years and the riot. I suppose that one day there will be an even newer and larger New York Infirmary, but that will be Emily's, not mine.

Using the connecting door I went into the next building, the College, walking slowly through the lecture rooms, empty in the evening hours; into the dissecting room where one lone young woman, bent over a partly covered cadaver, was learning of the beautiful intricacies of the human body. She reminded me of myself, those years ago, smuggled into La Charité in Paris, trying to see with my one good eye. Such studies are easier now, and I have helped to make them so.

I went up the stairs and visited each student's room in turn, exchanging a few words with these clear-eyed young women who will be tomorrow's doctors, the best doctors that training can turn out. I shall miss them all, but I can do no more for them here. There is still work for me, however, and—God willing —it should go more easily now.

Dear Mrs. Donaldson! How little either of us knew what your words to me would mean!

"Some woman is going to be the first female doctor, why should it not be you?"

Why not, indeed, Mrs. Donaldson! God bless you!

∾ *Epilogue*

∾Except for one or two brief visits to New York, Elizabeth Blackwell spent the last half of her life in England, which she always considered her home.

Working as hard there as she had in America, she maintained a private practice; was instrumental in founding the London School of Medicine for Women, in which she held the Chair of Gynecology; wrote and published several books, primarily on the moral education and physical health of the young; inspired and worked for the organization of the National Health Society; and, through her lectures, sowed the seeds for the White Slave Traffic Act.

When she was in her fifties Elizabeth Blackwell's health began to weaken from the strain of many years of intensive work, and at that time she purchased a house above the sea at Hastings, named, from its situation, Rock House. Although she gave up her practice, the next thirty years were quietly busy as she helped weak causes and inspired new ones, encouraged always by Kitty, who became—as the years went on—friend, companion, confidante and finally nursemaid.

Their favorite vacation spot was the village of Kilmun, in Argyllshire, Scotland, and they made frequent visits there. In 1907 Elizabeth Blackwell, then eighty-six, fell the length of the hotel stairs. Although no bones were broken, the shock to her system was so great that she never quite recovered from it. Returning to Rock House, she was unable to do intellectual work from then on, but she remained cheerful and deeply appreciative of the care given her and the visitors who came to see her. Often Kitty would find her sitting by the fire, smiling, and apparently deep in meditation. Surely there were sufficient memories to keep her less active mind contentedly occupied. To these she added a quiet and confident belief in a renewal of the spirit when her life would cease.

It did cease, softly and easily, on May 31, 1910, at the age of eighty-eight. In Kilmun a handsome Celtic cross marks her grave, and the epitaph contains the concluding statement from one of her lectures, "The Religion of Health."

In loving memory of Elizabeth Blackwell, M.D., born at Bristol 3rd February, 1821, died at Hastings 31st May, 1910. The first woman of modern times to graduate in medicine (1849) and the first to be placed on the British Medical Register (1859)

It is only when we have learned to recognise that God's law for the human body is as sacred —nay, is one with—God's law for the human soul that we shall begin to understand the religion of the heart.

Love seeketh not her own (I Cor. xiii. 5).
The pure in heart shall see God (Matt. v. 8).

✑ Bibliography

Blackwell, Elizabeth, *Pioneer Work in Opening the Medical Profession to Women.* New York: Collectors Editions, 1970

Chambers, Peggy, *A Doctor Alone.* New York: Abelard-Schuman, 1958

Glasscheib, H.S., *The March of Medicine.* New York: Putnam, 1964

Hays, Elinor Rice, *Those Extraordinary Blackwells.* New York: Harcourt, Brace, & World, 1967

Heyn, Leah Lurie, *Challenge to Become a Doctor.* Old Westbury, New York: The Feminist Press, 1971

James, Edward T., (ed.), *Notable American Women, 1607-1950: A Biographical Dictionary.* Cambridge, Massachusetts: The Belknap Press of Harvard University, 1971

Marks, Geoffrey and William K. Beatty, *Women in White.* New York: Charles Scribner's Sons, 1971

Ross, Ishbel, *Child of Destiny.* New York: Harper & Bros., 1949

Wilson, Dorothy Clarke, *Lone Woman.* Boston: Little, Brown and Co., 1970

Wyndham, Lloyd, *Hundred Years of Medicine.* New York: Humanities Press, 1968

❧ About the Author

Patricia Clapp's first novel, CONSTANCE: *A Story of Early Plymouth,* won a Lewis Carroll Shelf Award and was a runner-up for the 1968 National Book Award for Children's Literature. She is also the author of JANE-EMILY and has written over thirty plays for children. She is the Librarian for the New Jersey Theater League and a director of the Studio Playhouse of Essex County, New Jersey. She and her husband live in a large, old house in Upper Montclair, New Jersey.